101 GREAT
BOMBERS

101 GREAT BOMBERS

LEGENDARY FIGHTING AIRCRAFT FROM WWI TO THE PRESENT

Robert Jackson

Sandcastle Books

This edition published in 2008 by
Sandcastle Books Ltd
The Stables
Sheriffs Lench Court
Sheriffs Lench
Worcestershire
WR11 4SN
United Kingdom

M 10 9 8 7 6 5 4 3 2 1

ISBN-13: 978-1-906020-50-7

Editorial and design by
Amber Books Ltd
Bradley's Close
74–77 White Lion Street
London N1 9PF
United Kingdom
www.amberbooks.co.uk

Project Editor: Sarah Uttridge
Design: Graham Curd
Picture Research: Terry Forshaw and Kate Green

Picture Credits:
All photographs courtesy of **Art-Tech/Aerospace** except for the following:
Art-Tech/MARS: 36, 43, 46, 48, 56, 58, 83
Cody Images: 14, 17, 27, 29, 67
NASA Dryden Flight Research Center: 99
U.S. Department of Defense: 8-10, 85, 100-106, 108, 110
All artworks courtesy of **Art-Tech/Aerospace**

Printed in China

Contents

Introduction

The bomber had its genesis in World War I, when both sides used it to attack strategic targets. Bomber development then stagnated somewhat in the 1920s, but acquired new impetus in the following decade, when the major powers all produced new monoplane bomber designs. Whereas Britain and Japan strove to build long-range bombers, Germany, France and the United States concentrated on shorter-range types whose primary role was to act in support of ground forces.

Then, between 1939 and 1943, huge advances were made in the capability of bomber aircraft. From Britain and the United States came the heavy bombers that would take the war to the heart of Germany: the Lancaster and Halifax, the B-17 Flying Fortress and the B-24 Liberator. Between them, they would pound the Third Reich around the clock, the RAF by night and the USAAF by day. The ultimate in piston-engine bomber development during that bitter conflict was the Boeing B-29, which dropped two atomic bombs on Japan and brought World War II to a close. But by the end of the war Germany had produced the world's first jet bomber, the Arado Ar 234, and the air combat revolution had begun.

Trailing its characteristic clouds of black smoke, a Boeing B-52 thunders away on a mission.

The Northrop Grumman B-2 is designed to carry a formidable load of nuclear or conventional weapons, and to deliver them with great accuracy.

In the post-war world, Great Britain was first in the jet bomber field with the remarkable English Electric Canberra, an aircraft that was to remain in operational service with various air forces around the world for 56 years. Its longevity was rivalled only by the much heavier and larger Boeing B-52 Stratofortress and the latter's Russian equivalent, the Tupolev Tu-95 'Bear'. These aircraft, together with the Boeing B-47, the Tupolev Tu-16, and Britain's trio of 'V-bombers' – the Valiant, Vulcan and Victor – formed the nuclear deterrent forces of east and west during the most dangerous years of the Cold War. The war in Vietnam demonstrated the awesome striking power of the Boeing B-52 Stratofortress, but it also revealed the aircraft's vulnerability to surface-to-air missiles when it operated against the heaviest concentration of anti-aircraft weaponry in the world.

In other, later conflicts, the bomber that had been designed to replace the B-52 as the main sword of Strategic Air Command, the supersonic Rockwell B-1B, now found itself operating side by side with the veteran Boeing bomber in punitive operations over Afghanistan, assuming what amounted to an anti-terrorist role.

These conflicts have also seen the debut of new technology in the USAF's 'stealth' bombers, the F-117A and the B-2 Spirit, the latter flying the longest bombing operations in history during its operations in support of NATO and the United Nations.

This book is a history of the bomber from its beginnings to the present day, offering a detailed, chronological appraisal of 101 of the world's finest bombers, which have performed tactical and strategic bombing missions for their air forces during the past century.

The interdictor/strike version of the Panavia Tornado has the task of destroying high-value targets such as airfields and strategic bridges.

Caproni Ca.3

Caproni produced some of the best heavy bombers of World War I, and used them to begin a sustained air offensive against enemy targets.

COUNTRY OF ORIGIN: Italy

TYPE: four-seat heavy day bomber

POWERPLANT: three 100hp (75kW) Fiat A.10 6-cylinder piston engines

PERFORMANCE: maximum speed 116km/h (72mph); range 550km (340 miles)

WEIGHTS: empty 2500kg (5512lb); maximum take-off 3302kg (780lb)

DIMENSIONS: span 22.2m (72ft 10in); length 10.9m (35ft 9in); eight 3.7m (12ft 2in)

ARMAMENT: one or two 7.7mm Revelli machine guns on flexible mount in front cockpit; plus a maximum bomb load of 850kg (1874lb)

Both Italy and Russia had developed aircraft suitable for long-range bombing operations by the outbreak of World War I.

The Societa di Aviazione Ing Caproni in Italy and Igor Sikorsky in Russia showed remarkable foresight in producing the first heavy bombers. Caproni flew the Ca.30 bomber in 1913, at a time when the British had no explicit military aircraft and little compulsion to use them.

Early bombing raids

The Ca.30 had a short central nacelle with three 80hp (60kW) Gnome rotary engines, one driving a pusher screw, the others geared to tractor propellers on the tail booms. The later Ca.31 first flew in late 1914 with three 100hp (75kW) Fiat A.10 engines mounted on the front of the tail booms; it was put into production as the

Ca.1. Some 162 aircraft were produced before production switched to the Ca.2, with the central engine replaced by a 150hp (112kW) Isotta-Fraschini V.4B, and the main production variant, the Ca.3, with three Isotta-Fraschini V.4Bs. The latter gave rise to a post-war development, the 36M. The Ca.3 had a better performance and a greater bomb load; 164 Ca.2s and 269 Ca.3s were built. Caproni Ca.2s carried out the first Italian bombing raid of WWI, on 25 August 1914. The Italians undertook a sustained bombing offensive against the Austro-Hungarians, mostly at night. Caproni Ca.33s also equipped the Italian Naval Air Arm's first torpedo-bomber squadrons, as well as two squadrons of France's Aviation Militaire.

The immediate forerunner of the Caproni Ca.3 was the Ca.1, seen here in the markings of France's Aéronautique Militaire, 1916.

Gotha G.V

In the final year of World War I, Gotha bombers attacked targets in south-east England by both day and night in the first 'Battle of Britain'.

COUNTRY OF ORIGIN: Germany

TYPE: three-seat long-range biplane bomber

POWERPLANT: two 260hp (194kW) Mercedes D.IVa 6-cylinder inline piston engines

PERFORMANCE: maximum speed 140km/h (87mph); service ceiling 6500m (21,325ft); range 500km (310 miles)

WEIGHTS: empty 2740kg (6041lb); maximum take-off 3975kg (8763lb)

DIMENSIONS: span 23.7m (77ft 9in); length 11.86m (38ft 11in); height 4.3m (14ft 1in); wing area 89.5 sq m (963 sq ft)

ARMAMENT: two 7.92mm Parabellum machine guns on flexible mount in nose position; two 7.92mm Parabellum machine guns on flexible mount in dorsal position; plus maximum bomb load of 500kg (1102lb)

From August 1917 the earlier Gothas were gradually replaced by the new G.V, which carried a heavy defensive armament.

Alongside the airships and 'R' series from the Zeppelin works, the series of 'G' (Grossflugzeug, large aeroplane) designs from Gothaer Wagonfabrik played a major role in German strategic bombing in World War I. The G.I stemmed from a prototype built under the direction of Oskar Ursinus, a German Army major. Gotha built a small number under licence for tactical bombing over the Western and Eastern Fronts. The G.II was designed with the fuselage mounted on the lower rather than upper wing, and with nosewheels to prevent nosing over.

Cross-channel bombers

The G.II had a direct-drive Mercedes D.IVa, and a few had a tunnel extending to a rear gunner's cockpit that covered the previous defensive 'blind spot'. This was standard fitment on the G.IV, which first flew in December 1916 and was followed by a few G.V and G.Va aircraft, used for a short time before night-bombing was abandoned by the German Air Service in April 1918, by which time thirty-six Gothas were in service. Their typical bomb load on a cross-Channel raid was six 50kg (110lb) bombs. The G.Va and G.Vb differed from each other only in internal details, but could be distinguished from the G.V by their biplane tail assembly and shorter nose. In general, the Gotha bombers were agile for their size, well defended and difficult to shoot down.

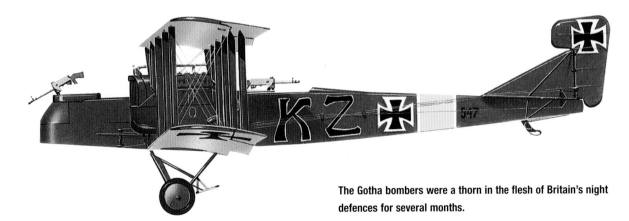

The Gotha bombers were a thorn in the flesh of Britain's night defences for several months.

Handley Page O/100 and O/400

The Handley page O/100 originated in a British requirement, issued in December 1914, for a 'bloody paralyser of an aeroplane' for the bombing of Germany. The nickname used it by its crews was entirely predictable.

Handley Page O/400 of No 207 Squadron, as seen at Ligescourt, France, in June 1918.

COUNTRY OF ORIGIN: United Kingdom

TYPE: three-seat heavy bomber biplane

POWERPLANT: two 360hp (268kW) Rolls-Royce Eagle VIII Vee-12 piston engines

PERFORMANCE: maximum speed 122km/h (76mph); service ceiling 2590m (8500ft); range with bomb load 724km (450 miles)

WEIGHTS: empty 3629kg (8000lb); loaded 6350kg (14,000lb)

DIMENSIONS: span 30.48m (100ft); length 19.16m (62ft 10in); height 6.7m (22ft); wing area 153.1sq m (1648 sq ft)

ARMAMENT: twin .303in Lewis guns on flexible mount in nose cockpit; one .303in Lewis gun on flexible mount in dorsal position; one .303in Lewis gun on flexible mount in ventral position; internal bomb bay with provision for eight 113kg (250lb) or 16 51kg (112lb) bombs

The O/100 adequately met, and in some cases exceeded, the tasks it was intended to perform. The O/100 first flew in December 1915 and entered service with No. 3 Wing of the Royal Naval Air Service in November 1916, and from the spring of the following year its two squadrons, Nos 14 and 16, mounted regular night attacks on major German installations, such as U-boat bases, railway yards and industrial complexes, operating from forward airfields on the Western Front.

Independent Bombing Force

From September 1917, many operations were flown against targets in the Saar. Fifty-six O/100s were delivered to the RNAS. In 1916 George Volkert modified the O/100 into the O/400 by moving the fuel tanks from the nacelles into the fuselage and fitting Rolls-Royce Eagle VIII engines. The other minor modification was the introduction of a compressed air engine starting system. Some 554 O/400s were built by British contractors with any one of four different engines fitted, namely the 284hp (212kW) Eagle IV, 360hp (268kW) Eagle VIII, 275hp (205kW) Sunbeam Maori or 350hp (261kW) Liberty 12. In the summer of 1918 the O/400 was the backbone of the newly formed Independent Bombing Force. Large formations of up to 40 aircraft mounted night attacks on German industrial areas and communications centres, ranging as far as Mannheim. By the end of the conflict O/400s were carrying 748kg (1650lb) bombs and also made a contribution to the campaign in Palestine.

This Handley Page O/400 was compelled to make a forced landing on enemy territory. It is seen here in German markings.

AEG G.IV

The AEG company produced some very effective aircraft during World War I. The G.IV bomber was one of the better short-range types.

COUNTRY OF ORIGIN: Germany

TYPE: four-seat bomber/reconnaissance biplane

POWERPLANT: two 260hp (194kW) Mercedes D.IVa inline engines

PERFORMANCE: maximum speed 165km/h (103mph); service ceiling 4500m (14,765ft); endurance 5hrs

WEIGHTS: empty 2400kg (5291lb); maximum take-off 3630kg (8003lb)

DIMENSIONS: span 18.4m (60ft 3in); length 9.7m (31 8in); height 3.9m (12ft 8in); wing area 67 sq m (721 sq ft)

ARMAMENT: one 7.92mm Parabellum machine gun on ring mounting in forward cockpit; one 7.92mm Parabellum machine gun on rail mounting in aft cockpit; underwing pylons for maximum bomb load of 400kg (882lb)

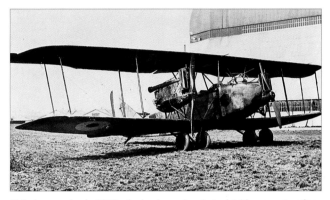

Entering service in 1916, of mixed wood and steel tubing construction, the AEG G.IV incorporated all the best features of its predecessors.

AEG undertook development of bomber aircraft for the German Kampfstaffel (battle squadrons) early in World War I. The first of the 'G' series, the G.I, was rather underpowered and only a single example was constructed. The following G.II and G.III suffered from the same problem and were therefore built in very small numbers.

Changing positions mid-flight

Marrying the powerplant of twin Mercedes D.IV engines to the airframe produced a far more effective aircraft in the form of the G.IV, but this did not enter service until the end of 1916. The four crew positions within the steel tube, fabric- and plywood-skinned aircraft were interconnected, enabling crew members to change position in flight as necessary. However, with a maximum bomb load and a crew of three, range was limited. Because of this and a fairly low operational ceiling, the G.IV was used mainly for tactical bombing, but in 1917 the units equipped with the type deployed to the southern front and began a lengthy series of night bombing attacks on Italian towns, such as Venice, Padua, Verona and Treviso. Returning to the Western Front in 1918, the G.IVs flew night bombing missions until the end of the war.

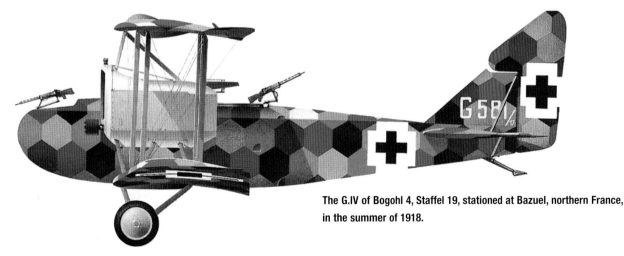

The G.IV of Bogohl 4, Staffel 19, stationed at Bazuel, northern France, in the summer of 1918.

Airco DH4

Designed by Geoffrey de Havilland, the DH4 has been described as the 'Mosquito' of World War I. It was extremely versatile.

COUNTRY OF ORIGIN: United Kingdom

TYPE: two-seat day bomber biplane (Westland-built, Eagle VI engine)

POWERPLANT: one 250hp (186kW) Rolls-Royce Eagle VI inline piston engine

PERFORMANCE: maximum speed 230km/h (143mph); service ceiling 6705m (22,000ft); endurance 3hrs 45mins

WEIGHTS: empty 1083kg (2387lb); maximum take-off 1575kg (3742lb)

DIMENSIONS: span 12.92m (42ft 4in); length 9.35m (30ft 8in); height 3.35m (11ft); wing area 40.32 sq m (434 sq ft)

ARMAMENT: two fixed forward-firing .303in Vickers machine guns and two .303in Vickers machine guns in rear cockpit; external pylons; provision for 209kg (460lb) of bombs

One of the most outstanding combat aircraft produced during World War I, the DH.4 day bomber was built in large numbers.

De Havilland designed the Airco D.H.4 around the 200 BHP (Beardmore-Halford-Pullinger) engine in response to an Air Ministry request for a new day bomber. Using an inline piston engine, de Havilland employed a clean tractor layout, breaking away from the traditional use of the rotary engine, but the wide separation between pilot and observer was a controversial and potentially dangerous feature because it hampered communication in the air. The 1449 British-built aircraft was built by various sub-contractors; delayed production of the BHP engine meant that other engines were employed on production aircraft.

Zeppelin destroyers

By spring 1918 the D.H.4 equipped nine RAF squadrons and was also in service with the Royal Naval Air Service. D.H.4s were engaged in the destruction of the flagship Zeppelin L.70. The bulk of DH.4 production took place in the USA, where 4846 aircraft were built by three companies. Many were powered by the 400hp Liberty 12 engine. Apart from serving with the US Army Air Service, DH.4s were widely used for civilian roles, for example, crop dusting and aerial survey.

A Rolls-Royce Eagle VI-engined aircraft of No. 5 (Naval) Squadron, RNAS.

Airco DH9/DH9A

The Airco DH9 was underpowered and inferior to the DH4, which it was supposed to replace. With a new engine, it became an excellent machine.

The DH.9 entered service with No. 103 Squadron RFC at Old Sarum, Wiltshire, in 1917, and became operational in France in 1918.

COUNTRY OF ORIGIN: United Kingdom

TYPE: two-seat day bomber biplane (American Liberty engine)

POWERPLANT: one 420hp (313kW) Packard Liberty 12 vee-12 piston engine

PERFORMANCE: maximum speed 198km/h (123mph); service ceiling 5105m (16,750ft); endurance 5hrs 15mins

WEIGHTS: empty 1270kg (2800lb); maximum take-off 2107kg (4645lb)

DIMENSIONS: span 14.01m (45ft 11in); length 9.22m (30ft 3in); height 3.45m (11ft 4in); wing area 45.22 sq m (487 sq ft)

ARMAMENT: one fixed forward-firing .303in Vickers machine gun and one or two .303in Lewis machine guns on Scarff ring in rear cockpit; external pylons with provision for 299kg (660lb) of bombs

Persistent German raids on Britain during World War I prompted a doubling in the size of the Royal Flying Corps, with most of the new squadrons equipped with day bombers. The D.H.4 was the expected type, but de Havilland had already attempted to rectify a glaring weakness of this aircraft by designing a modified version designated D.H.9 with the pilot and observer accommodated in back-to-back seating. This had a Siddeley Puma engine that could only produce 230hp (172kW), and performance of the early production D.H.9s was decidedly inferior to the D.H.4. In service with the RNAS and RFC from December 1917, the Puma engine was unreliable and the new aircraft that it

powered had a much reduced ceiling. But the DH.9 was quite a good fighting aeroplane once freed of its bomb load; this was partly due to the fact that the pilot and observer had better communication than in the DH.4.

Adding a Packard Liberty engine

By August 1918 RAF DH.9 squadrons in France were re-arming with the DH.9A which was powered by the US-built Packard Liberty engine. This improved the aircraft, and the DH.9A went on to perform a policing role.

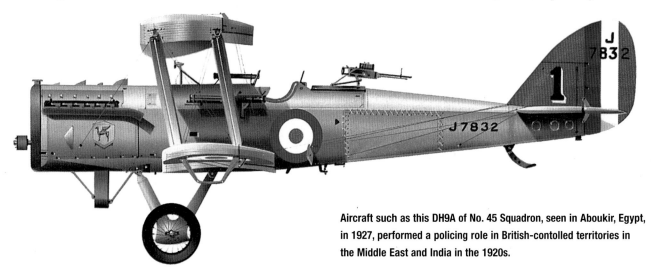

Aircraft such as this DH9A of No. 45 Squadron, seen in Aboukir, Egypt, in 1927, performed a policing role in British-contolled territories in the Middle East and India in the 1920s.

Breguet Br XIV

Louis Breguet's most effective product of World War I was without doubt the Br.XIV. The design of this two-seat reconnaissance/bomber was started in the late summer of 1916 by Breguet's Chief Engineer, Louis Vullierme, the prototype making its first flight on 21 November that year.

COUNTRY OF ORIGIN: France

TYPE: two-seat reconnaissance/light bomber biplane

POWERPLANT: one 300hp (224kW) Renault 12Fe inline piston engine

PERFORMANCE: maximum speed 184km/h (114mph); service ceiling 6000m (19,690ft); endurance 3hrs

WEIGHTS: empty 1030kg (2271lb); maximum take-off 1565kg (3450lb)

DIMENSIONS: span 14.36m (47ft 1in); length 8.87m (29ft 1in); height 3.3m (10ft 10in); wing area 47.50 sq m (530 sq ft)

ARMAMENT: one fixed forward-firing .303 machine gun; twin .303in Lewis machine guns on ring mounting in rear cockpit; underwing racks with provision for up 40kg (88lb) of bombs

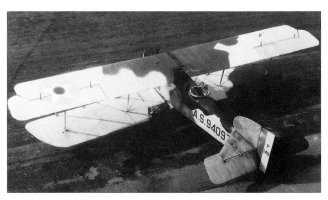

The first Br.XIVA-2 production aircraft entered service with the Aeronautique Militaire in the spring of 1917.

The first Br.XIVA-2 production aircraft entered service with the Aeronautique Militaire in the spring of 1917, and quickly established a tough and reliable reputation. It was the principal variant to serve with the French strategic day bombing force, which was completely transformed by the introduction of the new type. In all, Breguet XIVs served with 71 French Escadrilles on the Western Front, and also equipped five Escadrilles in Serbia, three in Greece, six in Morocco and eight in Macedonia. Two Belgian Escadrilles and several squadrons of the American Expeditionary Force also flew Breguet XIVs.

By the end of World War I, orders for the Breguet XIV had reached 5500 aircraft, ane rose to 8000 by 1926.

Variants included the unsuccessful BR.XIVH floatplane and the Br.XIVS air ambulance, which was used in small numbers during 1918. The Br.16Bn-2 was an enlarged night bomber version, while the Br.17C2 was a two-seat escort version with a 400hp Renault 12K engine and twin forward-firing Vickers machine guns. It came too late to see war service.

Setting new records

Post-war, the Breguet XIV was used by the French military and civil authorities, pioneering air routes in France's colonial empire. It set many records, including the first double crossing of the Mediterranean in 1919.

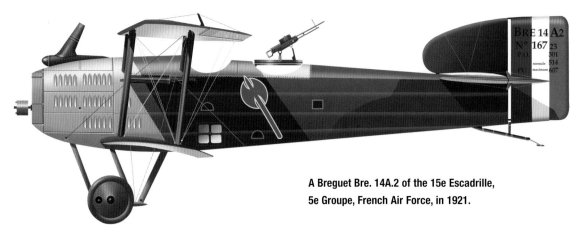

A Breguet Bre. 14A.2 of the 15e Escadrille, 5e Groupe, French Air Force, in 1921.

Zeppelin Staaken R Series

In late 1917 the massive Zeppelin R Type bombers joined the air offensive against England. Only two were lost in combat, but eight were destroyed in accidents.

COUNTRY OF ORIGIN: Germany

TYPE: heavy bomber

POWERPLANT: four 245hp Maybach Mb.IV 6-cylinder inline piston engines

PERFORMANCE: maximum speed 130km/h (81mph); service ceiling 3800m (12,500ft); range 800km (500 miles)

WEIGHTS: empty 7350kg (16,200lb); maximum take-off 11,460kg (25,265lb)

DIMENSIONS: span 42.2m (138ft 6in); length 22.1m (72ft 6in); height 6.3m (20ft 8in)

ARMAMENT: one or two 7.92mm Parabellum machine guns in nose position; one or two 7.92mm Parabellum machine guns in dorsal cockpit; one 7.92mm Parabellum machine gun in rear position; internal bay with provision for up to 18 100kg (220lb) bombs or one 1000kg (2205lb) bomb carried in semi-recessed position, up to a maximum load of 2000kg (4409lb)

British night fighter pilots found the Zeppelin Staaken R Types very difficult to shoot down.

The largest aircraft used in World War I were the sluggish but capable Riesenflugzeug (giant aeroplane) series produced by the Zeppelin Werke Staaken. Originally this organization had been Gotha, where the V.G.O.1, weighing 9000kg (19,850lb), first flew in April 1915 on the power of three 240hp (179kW) engines. Via several other one-off bombers, with three, four or five engines and different schemes of defensive armament, the design team of Baumann, Hirth and Klein eventually produced R.VI. Except for the V.G.O.I, which was lost in a crash, all of the giant bombers were used on the Eastern Front or against Britain. The VI went into production, one being built by the Staaken works, six by Aviatik, four by OAW, and seven by Schütte-Lanz. Three of the Aviatik machines had different noses, tails and Maybach engines.

Difficult to shoot down

The VI was followed by an assortment of derivatives, mainly powered by five Maybach engines, with varied airframes. The 'Giants' were extremely difficult to shoot down. For example, on the night of 30/31 January, 1918, the Zeppelin-Staaken R25 made it back to Ostend after surviving attacks by five fighters. They had collectively fired over 800 rounds at her, and after landing she was found to have taken no fewer than 88 hits. Sometimes, the Giant's sheer size led night fighter pilots to believe that they were firing from a much closer range than was actually the case.

The Zeppelin-Staaken R types joined Gothas in attacks in targets in France, where occasionally they caused substantial damage to fuel and ammunition dumps.

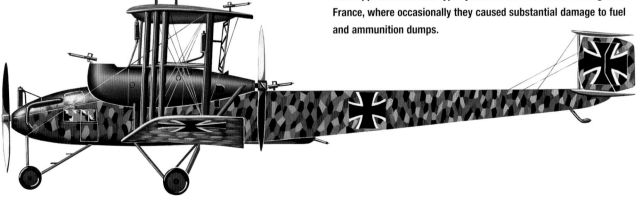

Vickers Vimy

In the closing stages of World War I Vickers produced a large biplane bomber, the FB.27 Vimy, with the object of attacking Berlin. It was ordered into large-scale production for the newly formed Independent Force, the RAF's strategic bombing force.

The Vimy is best remembered for its long-range pioneering flights, including the crossing of the Atlantic by Alcock and Brown in 1919.

COUNTRY OF ORIGIN: United Kingdom

TYPE: heavy bomber

POWERPLANT: two 360hp (269kW) Rolls-Royce Eagle VIII 12-cylinder Vee piston engines

PERFORMANCE: maximum speed 166km/h (103mph); service ceiling 2135m (7000ft);range 1464km (910 miles)

WEIGHTS: empty 3221kg (7101lb); maximum take-off 5670kg (12,500lb)

DIMENSIONS: span 20.75m (68ft 1in); length 13.27m (43ft 6in); height 4.76m (15ft 7in); wing area 123.56 sq m (1330 sq ft)

ARMAMENT: one .303in Lewis Mk III machine gun on pivoted mount in nose; one .303in Lewis Mk III machine gun on pivoted mount in dorsal position; one .303in Lewis Mk III machine gun on pivoted mount in ventral or each of two beam positions; internal bomb cells and underwing racks with provision for up to 2179kg (4804lb) of bombs

The Vimy showed exceptional handling qualities and proved capable of lifting a greater load than the Handley Page O/400 on half the power. Production of the Vimy Mk I totalled 158 aircraft, deliveries to RAF bomber squadrons beginning in July 1919. It was withdrawn from the bomber role in 1924, but many served on with various training establishments and parachute schools, the last military Vimy being retired from No. 4 Flying Training School at Abu Sueir, Egypt, in 1933. The Vimy was the first aircraft to cross the Atlantic, flown by Capt John Alcock and Lt Arthur Whitten Bown in 1919. The Vimy Mk III (10 built by RAE at Farnborough) and Mk IV (25 built by Westland) had Rolls-Royce Eagle engines and minor detail changes. The designation Vimy Mk II is most confusing, as it appears to have been given to many different types. To confuse matters further, the Mk III and Mk IV were redesignated Mk II in 1923, for clarity.

Standard heavy bomber

What is clear is that the Vimy was the standard heavy bomber of the RAF from 1919 to 1930, after which it began to be replaced by the Vickers Victoria. Most of the RAF aircraft were sent overseas to act as a tool of the RAF's air policing operations in the Middle East, where Nos 45, 58, 70 and 216 Sqns and No. 4 Flying Training School were operating.

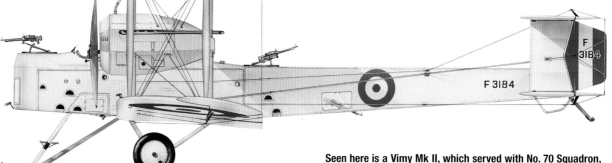

Seen here is a Vimy Mk II, which served with No. 70 Squadron, Heliopolis, Egypt. No. 70 Squadron used the Vimy from 1920 to 1922.

Handley Page Heyford

The Handley Page Heyford was the last of the RAF's biplane bombers, and was of unusual configuration in that the upper wing was attached to the fuselage.

COUNTRY OF ORIGIN: United Kingdom

TYPE: heavy night-bomber

POWERPLANT: two 575hp (429kW) Rolls-Royce Kestrel IIIS 12-cylinder Vee-piston engine

PERFORMANCE: maximum speed 229km/h (142mph); service ceiling 6400m (21,000ft); range with 726kg (1600lb) bomb load 1481kg (920 miles)

WEIGHTS: empty 4173kg (9200lb); maximum take-off 7666kg (16,900lb)

DIMENSIONS: span 22.86m (75ft); length 17.68m (58ft); height 5.33m (17ft 6in); wing area 136.56 sq m (1470 sq ft)

ARMAMENT: one .303in Lewis machine gun on flexible mount in nose position; one .303in Lewis machine gun on flexible mount in dorsal position; one .303in Lewis machine gun on flexible mount in ventral turret; internal bay with provision for up to 1588kg (3500lb) of bombs

The ungainly Handley Page Heyford provided RAF crews with valuable night flying experience.

When it first appeared in 1930 the ungainly appearance of the H.P.50 was roundly derided, yet this aircraft formed the backbone of Britain's so-called strategic bombing fleet in the 1930s and soldiered on until more capable types were introduced. Its clumsy appearance was compounded by its unusual configuration, with shoulder-mounted biplane wing. Handley Page designers reasoned that incorporating a bomb bay into this lower wing would reduce the time required for re-arming.

Rolls-Royce Kestrel power

Power was provided by two Rolls-Royce Kestrels in nacelles mounted beneath the upper wing, and for defence there were three fuselage-mounted machine guns, one in a retractable dustbin turret. The RAF took delivery of 124 H.P.50s as Heyford Mks I, II and IIIs, which differed mainly in installed powerplant. Eleven squadrons were equipped with the type; by 1939 they had all re-equipped with Vickers Wellingtons, and the Heyford was relegated to training. The Heyford was cumbersome and soon outmoded, yet it underpinned the RAF's bomber force during the crucial expansion period of the early 1930s, and its widespread use enabled the RAF to develop night-bombing techniques that would be put to use in the early months of World War II.

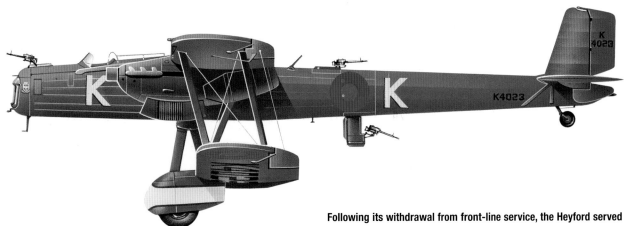

Following its withdrawal from front-line service, the Heyford served in various training roles until early part of World War II.

Martin B-10 and B-12

It was obsolete by the outbreak of World War II, but the Martin B-10 was a very advanced aircraft when it first appeared in 1932.

COUNTRY OF ORIGIN: USA

TYPE: (Model 139W) four-seat medium bomber

POWERPLANT: two 775hp (578kW) Wright R-1820 G-102 Cyclone 9-cylinder single-row radial engines

PERFORMANCE: maximum speed 322km/h (200mph); initial climb rate 567m (1860ft) per minute; service ceiling 7680m (25,200ft); range 950km (590 miles) with maximum bomb load

WEIGHTS: empty 4682kg (10,322lb); maximum take-off 7210kg (15,894lb)

DIMENSIONS: span 21.60 m (70ft 10.5in); length 13.46m (44ft 2in); height 3.53m (11ft 7in)

ARMAMENT: one 0.3in trainable forward-firing machine gun in nose turret, one 0.3in trainable rearward-firing machine gun in dorsal position, and one 0.3in trainable rearward-firing machine gun in the ventral position, plus an internal and external bomb load of 1025kg (2260lb)

The Martin B-10 was the first American bomber of all-metal construction to enter full production.

The first US-designed bomber to be flown in combat (but by an overseas air force), the B-10 bomber series was obsolete by the beginning of World War II, but in its time was a pioneering type. It was the first American bomber of all-metal construction to enter large-scale production, the first American warplane to be fitted with turreted armament, and the US Army Air Corps' first cantilever low-wing monoplane. The USAAC received 151 examples of the B-10 and B-12 bombers, all retired before World War II, but some export aircraft saw combat service.

Exporting the model

The basic Model 139 was exported to Argentina, China, Thailand and Turkey. The Japanese fought against the Chinese machines as well as the 120 Model 139W and Model 166 aircraft of the Netherlands East Indies in the late 1930s and early 1940s. The B-10's principal rival was the Boeing B-9, the first US aircraft to feature servo tabs mounted on the movable control surfaces to assist the pilots to overcome increased loads at top speed. Sadly for Boeing, the Air Corps ordered only six aircraft plus the prototype; the big contract went to the Glenn L. Martin Company's B-10 bomber, which was to be the backbone of the Air Corps' bomber arm for a decade to come.

The Martin Model 123, also designated XB-907, was used for operational trials and was the forerunner of the definitive B-10 bomber.

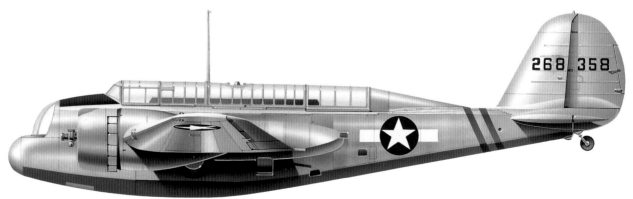

Vickers Vildebeest

The Vickers Vildebeest was obsolete at the outbreak of World War II, and its crews paid a heavy price when they were pitted against Japanese Zero fighters in 1941.

COUNTRY OF ORIGIN: United Kingdom

TYPE: three-seat general-purpose aircraft

POWERPLANT: one 660hp (492kW) Bristol Pegasus IIM3 sleeve-valve radial piston engine

PERFORMANCE: maximum speed 230km/h (142mph); service ceiling 5182m (17,000ft); range 2500km (1553 miles)

WEIGHTS: empty 1918kg (4229lb); maximum take-off 3674kg (8100lb)

DIMENSIONS: span 14.94m (49ft in); length 11.17m (36ft 8in); height 5.42m (17ft 9in)

ARMAMENT: one fixed forward-firing .303in Vickers machine gun; one .303in Lewis machine gun on pivoted mount in rear cockpit

In 1942, Vildebeests based on Singapore suffered nearly 100 per cent losses in attacks on Japanese shipping.

In 1927 the British Air Ministry needed a new light bomber to replace the Hawker Horsley torpedo/day bomber, which entered service that year. The Vickers Vildebeest fulfilled this, and was flown as the Type 132 prototype in April 1928.

Tragedy in the Far East

Development with a number of engines was followed by the initial Mk I production model with Bristol Pegasus I for service delivery in April 1933. There were 152 aircraft in the first three series. In December 1937 the last of 57 Mk IVs were delivered. About 100 Vildebeests were still serving at the outbreak of World War II, and were used in the Far East. When Japanese amphibious forces began landing on the coast of Malaya in December 1941, Nos 36 and 100 Squadrons, based on Singapore, were still using Vildebeests. On 8 December, No. 36 Squadron attempted unsuccessfully to attack enemy warships. On 26 January 1942, the Japanese landed at Endau, Malaya. Vildebeests attacked the enemy transports of Endau; five Vildebeests were shot down. Nine Vildebeests of No. 36 Squadron launched a second attack. All were destroyed.

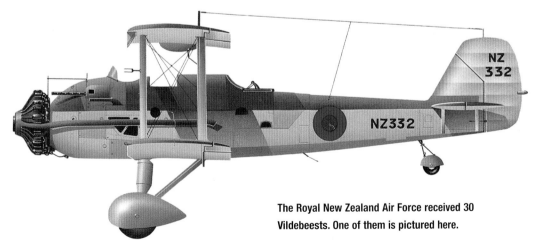

The Royal New Zealand Air Force received 30 Vildebeests. One of them is pictured here.

Fairey Swordfish

The Fairey Swordfish appeared to be an anachronism; a slow, lumbering biplane with no place in the world of 1930s aviation. Yet the design of the Swordfish was exactly right for the principal tasks it had to perform.

COUNTRY OF ORIGIN: United Kingdom

TYPE: (Swordfish Mk I) three-seat carrierborne and land-based torpedo bomber, level bomber and reconnaissance aeroplane

POWERPLANT: one 775hp (578kW) Bristol Pegasus IIIM3 nine-cylinder single-row radial engine

PERFORMANCE: maximum speed 224km/h (139mph); climb to 1525m (5000ft) in 10 minutes 30 seconds; ceiling 3780m (12,400ft); range 1657km (1030 miles)

WEIGHTS: empty 2359kg (5200lb); maximum take-off 4196kg (9250lb)

DIMENSIONS: span 13.87m (45ft 6in); length 11.07m (36ft 4in) with the tail up; height 4.11m (13ft 5.75in) with the tail up

ARMAMENT: one 0.303in fixed forward-firing machine gun in the starboard side of the forward fuselage, and one 0.303in trainable rearward-firing machine in the rear cockpit; external bomb load of 726kg (1600lb)

This Fairey Swordfish is maintained in immaculate condition by the Royal Navy's Historic Flight at Yeovilton, in Somerset.

The Swordfish was one of the finest warplanes of World War II. This reputation resulted from its biplane airframe, ruggedness, reliability, versatility in terms of weapons and equipment, and such perfect handling characteristics that it could be flown in most weather conditions from the largest fleet carriers to the smallest of escort carriers.

Carrierborne 'Stringbag'

The type, universally known as the 'Stringbag', resulted from a 1930 requirement for a carrierborne aeroplane to serve in the spotter, reconnaissance and torpedo attack roles. The first of four prototype and pre-production aircraft flew in March 1933. Successful trials led to orders for an eventual 989 aircraft. Fairey built 689 and the remainder were Blackburn-built machines. Service deliveries began in July 1936 and by the beginning of World War II the FAA had 13 operational Swordfish squadrons. The Swordfish served with great distinction in World War II, from the North Atlantic to the Indian Ocean, and in so doing performed feats of arms that became legendary. Notable Swordfish actions included the Battle of Cape Matapan in March 1941, the crippling of the German battleship *Bismarck* in May, and the gallant action against the *Scharnhorst*, *Gneisenau* and *Prinz Eugen* during the famous 'Channel Dash' of February 1942. At that time, all six Swordfish of No. 825 Squadron involved were shot down and their commander, Lt Cdr Eugene Esmonde, was awarded a posthumous Victoria Cross.

The Swordfish's open cockpit did not make for crew comfort, especially during operations in Arctic waters.

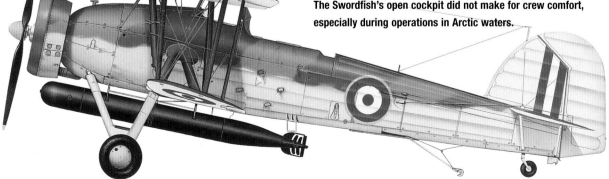

Hawker Hind

The Hawker Hind began to replace the Hart as the RAF's standard light bomber late in 1935. An improved Hart with a more powerful engine and refined aerodynamics, the prototype Hind first flew on 12 September 1934.

COUNTRY OF ORIGIN: United Kingdom

TYPE: two-seat light day-bomber

POWERPLANT: one 640hp (477kW) Rolls-Royce Kestrel V 12-cylinder Vee piston engine

PERFORMANCE: maximum speed 298km/h (184mph); service ceiling 8045m (26,400ft); range 692km (430 miles)

WEIGHTS: empty 1475kg (3251lb); maximum take-off 2403kg (5298lb)

DIMENSIONS: span 11.35m (37ft 3in); length 9.02m (29ft 7in); height 3.23m (10ft 7in); wing area 32.33 sq m (348 sq ft)

ARMAMENT: one fixed-forward firing .303in Vickers Mk II machine gun; one .303in Lewis machine gun on pivoted mount in rear cockpit; underwing racks with provision for up to 227kg (500lb) of bombs

Hawker Hind K5414 is maintained and flown by the Shuttleworth Collection, Bedfordshire.

Air Ministry Specification G.7/34 called for a light bomber that could serve as an interim replacement for the Hawker Hart until more modern types such as the Bristol Blenheim and Fairey Battle began to enter service. Sidney Camm proposed an updated version of the Hart, powered by a 640hp (477kW) Kestrel V engine. Other features were a cut-down rear cockpit with a better field of fire for the observer, and a tailwheel in place of the skid.

Serving with air forces internationally

The prototype Hind was flown in September 1934 and was followed by 527 production aircraft, which served in no fewer than 47 RAF bomber squadrons between 1935 and 1939. The Hind also served with the air forces of Afghanistan, Eire, India, Kenya, Latvia, New Zealand and Persia. Many RAF Hinds were converted for training, including the example pictured, which served with No. 1 Flying Training School in the early war years. The aircraft the Hind was intended to replace, the Hawker Hart, was the most widely used RAF light bomber of the 1930s. The prototype flew in June 1928 and deliveries of the first production aircraft began in January 1930. A trainer version of the Hart was also produced, as was the Hart C general-purpose aircraft, the Hart Special and the Hart India, both of which were tropicalized versions. Eight Harts were exported to Estonia and four to Sweden, which built a further 24 Harts under licence, these being powered by Pegasus radial engines. Faster than any contemporary RAF fighter, the Hart excelled in India's harsh North-West Frontier climate.

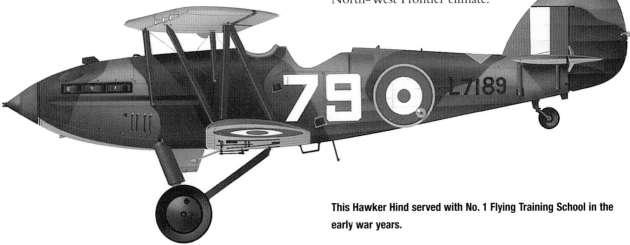

This Hawker Hind served with No. 1 Flying Training School in the early war years.

Junkers Ju 52/3m

Although it was to become famous as a transport aircraft, the Junkers Ju 52 3/m began life as a bomber, and operated in that role in the Spanish Civil War.

This Ju 52/3m was used by the Swiss national airline, Swissair, in its original role as a passenger aircraft.

COUNTRY OF ORIGIN: Germany

TYPE: (Ju 52/3m g7e) three-seat transport with accommodation for 18 troops, or 12 litters, or freight

POWERPLANT: three 730hp (544kW) BMW 132T-2 nine-cylinder radial engines

PERFORMANCE: maximum speed 286km/h (178mph); climb to 3000m (9845ft) in 17 minutes 30 seconds; service ceiling 5900m (19,360ft); range 1305km (811 miles)

WEIGHTS: empty 6500kg (14,328lb); maximum take-off 11,030kg (24,317lb)

DIMENSIONS: span 29.20m (95ft 10in); length 18.90m (62ft); height 4.52m (14ft 10in)

ARMAMENT: one 13mm or 7.92mm trainable rearward-firing machine gun in rear dorsal position, provision for one 7.92mm trainable machine gun in forward dorsal position, and one 7.92mm trainable lateral-firing machine gun in each of the two beam positions

A successor to the W 33 and W 34 transports, the Ju 52 was planned from the late 1920s as an enlarged version of the same basic design, and first flew in prototype form in October 1930 with one 725hp (541kW) BMW VII Vee engine. The Ju 52a to Ju 52d initial production models for the civil market differed only in the type of engine used, but with the Ju 52/3m a three-engined powerplant was introduced for greater payload and performance.

Operating on every front

The series extended to 4850 aircraft, the vast majority of them to meet military orders in variants between the Ju 52/3m ge and the Ju 52/3m g14e. The Ju 52/3m served initially as a bomber as well as transport, but in World War II was a transport and airborne forces aeroplane that saw operational use in every German theatre up to May 1945. In April 1940 the Ju 52 was at the forefront of the invasions of Denmark and Norway. About 475 Ju 52s were available for the invasion of the Netherlands, and 493 took part in the invasion of Crete in May 1941. By the end of the year around 300 Ju 52s were in the Mediterranean theatre. German transport aircraft, mostly Ju 52s, were destroyed for the loss of 35 Allied fighters. On the Russian front, five Ju 52 Gruppen took part in the Stalingrad airlift. The total production of the Ju 52/3m between 1939 and 1944, including civil models, amounted to 4845 aircraft.

The Ju 523/m shown here carries the code letters of Transportgeschwader 1.

PZL P.23 Karas

The PZL P.23 Karas (Carp) prototype flew for the first time in August 1934. The major production version, appearing in 1936, was the P-23B Karas-B reconnaissance-bomber.

COUNTRY OF ORIGIN: Poland

TYPE: (P.23B Karas) three-seat light reconnaissance bomber

POWERPLANT: one 680hp (507kW) PZL (Bristol) Pegasus VIII nine-cylinder single-row radial engine

PERFORMANCE: maximum speed 300km/h (186mph); climb to 2000m (6560ft) in 4 minutes 45 seconds; service ceiling 7300m (23,950ft); range 1400km (870 miles)

WEIGHTS: empty 1928kg (4250lb); maximum take-off 3526kg (7773lb)

DIMENSIONS: span 13.95m (45ft 9.25in); length 9.68m (31ft 9.25in); height 3.30m (10ft 10in)

ARMAMENT: one 7.7mm fixed forward-firing machine gun in the forward fuselage, one 7.7mm trainable rearward-firing machine gun with 600 rounds in the rear cockpit, and one 7.7mm machine gun in the ventral position, plus an external bomb load of 700kg (1543lb)

Like other modern Polish combat aircraft, the Karas came too late to be of much value in combat when the Germans invaded.

Stemming from the P.13 project for a six-passenger transport, the P.23 Karas (Crucian Carp) was a light bomber and army co-operation warplane. The P.23/I Karas was the first of three prototypes and flew in August 1934. The type was ordered into production as the P.23A trainer with the 590hp (440kW) Pegasus IIM2 engine and P.23B operational model with an uprated engine (40 and 210 aircraft respectively). With their fixed landing gear, indifferent performance and poor armament, the aircraft suffered heavy losses in the German invasion of September 1939 before 31 survivors were flown to Romania. Another 54 aircraft were delivered to Bulgaria in two P.43 variants with Gnome-Rhône radial engines.

Valiant gallantry

Polish light bomber crews of Nos 64 and 65 Squadrons, flying eighteen Karas aircraft, attacked concentrations of German armour on the northern front on 2 September 1939. They inflicted heavy casualties, but severe light flak and enemy fighters destroyed seven Karas and three of those that returned to base crashed on landing. In one mission, the bombers had suffered over 50 per cent losses.

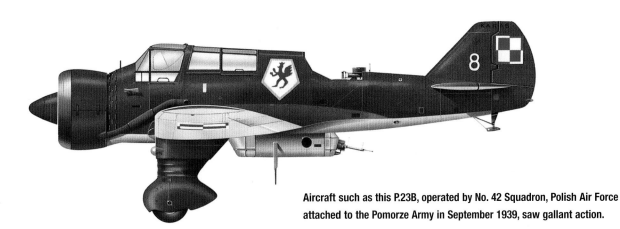

Aircraft such as this P.23B, operated by No. 42 Squadron, Polish Air Force attached to the Pomorze Army in September 1939, saw gallant action.

Tupolev SB-2

The story of the SB-2 (the initials stand for Skorostnoy Bombardirovshchik, or high-speed bomber) began in the early 1930s, when Andrei N. Tupolev embarked on design studies of a fast tactical bomber.

COUNTRY OF ORIGIN: USSR

TYPE: (SB-2bis) three-seat light bomber

POWERPLANT: two 960hp (716kW) Klimov M-103 12-cylinder Vee engines

PERFORMANCE: maximum speed 450km/h (280mph); climb to 1000m (3280ft) in 1 minute 48 seconds; service ceiling 9000m (29,530ft); range 2300km (1429 miles)

WEIGHTS: empty 4768kg (10,511lb); maximum take-off 7880kg (17,372lb)

DIMENSIONS: span 20.33m (66ft 8.5in); length 12.57m (41ft 2.75in); height 3.25m (10ft 8in)

ARMAMENT: two 7.62mm trainable forward-firing machine guns in the nose position, one 7.62mm trainable rearward-firing machine gun in the dorsal turret, and one 7.62mm trainable rearward-firing machine gun in the ventral position, plus an internal bomb load of 600kg (1323lb)

Several SB-2s, like the example seen here, were captured by the Finns during the 'winter war' and pressed into service.

The SB-2 was the most capable bomber serving anywhere in the world during the mid-1930s. In purely numerical terms it was the most important bomber in the world during the late 1930s, and was also the first 'modern' aeroplane of the stressed-skin type to enter production in the USSR, an event that took place in 1935. Considering the official requirement to be inadequate, Tupolev built two prototypes according to the Air Force Technical Office specification, and a third according to his own.

Tupolev ANT-40-2

All three prototypes, designated ANT-40, ANT-40-1 and ANT-40-2, flew in 1934. Tupolev's own version, the ANT-40-2, proved the best. It was ordered into production, entering service in 1936, and 6967 aircraft were built by 1941. The SB-2 was initially delivered with 730hp (544kW) M-100 engines driving fixed-pitch propellers, but then came the 860hp (641kW) M-100A engine in a wider nacelle and driving a variable-pitch propeller. SB-2 series production totalled 6967 aircraft, and the most important variant was the SB-2bis with uprated and different engines and greater fuel capacity. Other variants included 200 SB-RK dive-bombers with 1100hp (820kW) Klimov M-105R engines, and the 111 Czechoslovak licence-built B 71 bombers.

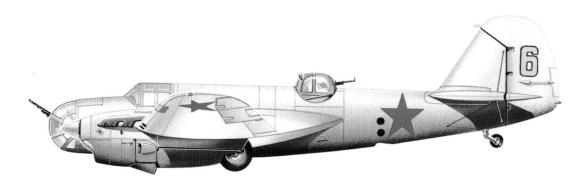

An SB-2bis of the Red Air Force, wearing the winter camouflage used in the 1939-40 campaign against Finland.

Savoia-Marchetti SM.79 Sparviero

Fast, well armed and with a good range, the SM.79 was used to good effect during the Italian campaign in Abyssinia, in October 1935, and from August 1936 it was also used operationally during the Spanish Civil War.

Of all its varied roles, the SM.79 Sparviero ('Sparrowhawk') was perhaps at its best as a torpedo bomber, seen here.

COUNTRY OF ORIGIN: Italy

TYPE: (SM.79-I) four/five-seat medium reconnaissance bomber

POWERPLANT: three 780hp (582kW) Alfa Romeo 126 RC.34 9-cylinder single-row radial engines

PERFORMANCE: maximum speed 430km/h (267mph); climb to 5000m (16,405ft) in 19 minutes 45 seconds; service ceiling 6500m (21,325ft); range 1900km (1181 miles) with a 1250kg (2756lb) bomb load

WEIGHTS: empty 6800kg (14,991lb); maximum take-off 10,480kg (23,104lb)

DIMENSIONS: span 21.20m (69ft 2.7in); length 15.62m (51ft 3.1in); height 4.40m (14ft 5.25in)

ARMAMENT: one 12.7mm fixed forward-firing machine gun above cockpit, one 12.7mm trainable rearward-firing machine gun in dorsal position, one 12.7mm machine gun in ventral position, and one 7.7mm machine gun in two beam positions; bomb load of 2756lb (1250kg)

Arguably one of the finest torpedo bombers of World War II, it had a three-engined layout and 'hunchback' fuselage. First flown in 1934 as the SM.79P civil transport prototype with eight-passenger seating, it was developed as a medium reconnaissance bomber and entered service as the SM.79-I with the uprated powerplant of three Alfa Romeo 126 radial engines and a large ventral gondola. The following SM.79-II was optimized for the anti-ship role with two 450mm torpedoes and a powerplant of three 1000hp (746kW) Piaggio P.XI RC.40 or 1030hp (768kW) Fiat A.80 RC.41 radial engines. The final Italian model was the SM.79-III improved SM.79-II with heavier defensive armament but no ventral gondola. The SM.79B, first flown in 1936, was a twin-engined export model, the middle engine being replaced by an extensively glazed nose. Brazil took delivery of three, Iraq four, and Romania 48, each version with a different powerplant.

Serving on the Eastern Front

The Romanian IAR factories also built 1230 SM.79B aircraft under licence, with Junkers Jumo 211D engines, and used the aircraft in bomber and transport roles on the Eastern Front. The aircraft stayed in service post-war as a transport with the Aeronautica Militare Italiana.

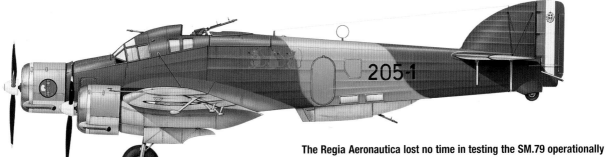

The Regia Aeronautica lost no time in testing the SM.79 operationally in Spain, where the type was used with considerable success by the 8ø and 111ø Stormi Bombardamento Veloce (High Speed Bomber Groups).

Dornier Do 17

Nicknamed the 'Flying Pencil' because of its slender fuselage, the Do 17 was poorly armed and suffered badly when it came up against the RAF's fighters in the Battle of Britain.

COUNTRY OF ORIGIN: Germany

TYPE: (Do 17E-1) three/four-seat light bomber

POWERPLANT: two 750hp (559kW) BMW VI 7,3 12-cylinder Vee engines

PERFORMANCE: maximum speed 355km/h (221mph); service ceiling 5100m (16,730ft); radius 500km (311 miles) with maximum bomb load

WEIGHTS: empty 4500kg (9921lb); maximum take-off 7040kg (15,520lb)

DIMENSIONS: span 18.00m (59ft 0.67in); length 16.25m (53ft 3.5in); height 4.32m (14ft 2in)

ARMAMENT: one 7.92mm trainable forward-firing machine gun in the starboard side of the cockpit, provision for one 7.92mm trainable forward-firing machine gun in the lower nose, one 7.92mm trainable rearward-firing machine gun in the rear of the cockpit, one 7.92mm rearward-firing machine gun; internal bomb load of 750kg (1653lb)

This view of a Dornier 17 with its slender fuselage clearly shows how it acquired its nickname of the 'Flying Pencil'.

Designed as a fast mailplane for Deutsche Lufthansa and first flown in 1934, the Do 17 was rejected in its planned role after the delivery of three single-finned aircraft, and was then developed via 12 prototypes as a high-speed bomber with twin vertical tail surfaces.

High-speed bombing

Entering service in the first months of 1937, the first two military variants of the 'Flying Pencil' were the Do 17E-1 and Do 17F-1, intended for the high-speed bomber and long-range photo-reconnaissance roles respectively, the latter with additional fuel and the internal bomb bay revised for the carriage of two cameras. Faster than most contemporary fighters when it entered service, the Do 17 soon became obsolescent and suffered heavy losses in the battles of France and Britain. The Do 17K was an export version for Yugoslavia, where it was built under licence; some were later handed over to the Croatian Air Force. The Do 215 was another export version, 100 of which were taken over by the Luftwaffe early in World War II.

The Finnish Air Force received some Do 17s during World War II. This example is seen in post-war Finnish insignia.

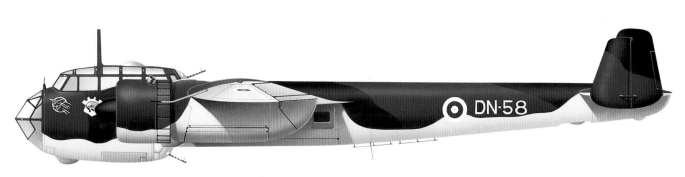

Amiot 143

The Amiot 143 was quite an advanced bomber design when it was first conceived, but it was hopelessly outclassed by the time of the outbreak of World War II.

COUNTRY OF ORIGIN: France

TYPE: (Amiot 143M.4) four/six-seat night bomber and reconnaissance warplane

POWERPLANT: two 870hp (640kW) Gnome-Rhône 14Kirs/Kjrs Mistral-Major 14-cylinder two-row radial engines

PERFORMANCE: maximum speed 310km/h (193mph); climb to 4000m (13,125ft) in 14 minutes 20 seconds; service ceiling 7900m (25,920ft); range 2000km (1243 miles)

WEIGHTS: empty 6100kg (13,448lb); maximum take-off 9700kg (21,385lb)

DIMENSIONS: span 24.53m (80ft 5.75in); length 18.26m (59ft 11in); height 5.68m (18ft 7.75in)

ARMAMENT: up to six 7.5mm machine guns, plus an internal and external bomb load of 1600kg (3527lb)

The Amiot 143 was a re-engined version of the Amiot 140, the first of 135 examples delivered to the Armée de l'Air in the middle of 1935.

First flown in April 1931, the Amiot 140 was designed to meet a 1928 requirement for a plane that could be used as day and night bomber, for long-range reconnaissance, and as a bomber escort. It was ordered into production in November 1934 with Lorraine W-type engines, and the plane became the Amiot 143 with the powerplant changed to Gnome-Rhône engines.

Obsolete but still in service

The Amiot 143M.4 entered service in 1935, and 138 aircraft were built, the later examples with 7.5mm MAC 1934 machine guns, a longer nose, and fixed rather than jettisonable auxiliary fuel tanks. This obsolete type still equipped six groupes de bombardement at the start of World War II. From the outset of hostilities the Amiots of the 34e Escadre were engaged in leaflet-dropping activities. Many flew bombing missions against German targets, and suffered heavy losses while operating in daylight against the Sedan bridgeheads. Fifty Amiot 143s remained in first-line service on 24 June 1940, although in the later stages of the French campaign they had been restricted to night operations. The surviving aircraft were operated as transports to Vichy French forces in North Africa until 1944.

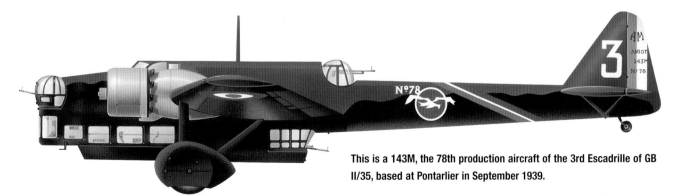

This is a 143M, the 78th production aircraft of the 3rd Escadrille of GB II/35, based at Pontarlier in September 1939.

Bristol Blenheim

A fast and agile bomber when it first appeared, the Blenheim was soon overtaken by aviation technology and became very vulnerable to enemy fighter attack.

This neat formation of Blenheim Mk IV bombers feature the roundels that were in use prior to the outbreak of war.

COUNTRY OF ORIGIN: United Kingdom

TYPE: (Blenheim Mk I) three-seat light bomber

POWERPLANT: two 840hp (627kW) Bristol Mercury VIII nine-cylinder single-row radial engines

PERFORMANCE: maximum speed 459km/h (285mph); climb to 4570m (15,000ft) in 9 minutes 58 seconds; service ceiling 8315m (27,280ft); range 1810km (1125 miles)

WEIGHT: empty 4013kg (8839lb); maximum take-off 5947kg (13,100lb)

DIMENSIONS: span 17.17m (56ft 4in); length 12.12m (39ft 9in); height 3m (9ft 10in)

ARMAMENT: one 0.303in fixed forward-firing machine gun in the leading edge of the port wing, and one 0.303in trainable machine gun in the dorsal turret, plus an internal bomb load of 454kg (1000lb)

A militarized version of the Type 142 high-speed light transport, the Type 142M prototype paved the way for the Blenheim Mk I light bomber that entered service in 1939. The RAF hoped this aircraft would provide operational capability as well as help create a pool of skilled aircrews.

Fighting on both sides

It saw extensive service but never was truly effective; the first variant was the Blenheim Mk I, and 1365 were built by three British manufacturers, 45 and 16 similar aircraft being built in Finland and Yugoslavia respectively. In addition a small number were presented to Romania in 1939, with the result that the Blenheim fought both for and against the Allies. Some British aircraft were converted to Blenheim Mk IF night-fighter standard with a ventral pack of four 0.303in machine guns and radar. When war broke out, the home-based squadrons re-armed with the Blenheim Mk IV. Twelve Blenheims were supplied to Finland (which built another 55 between 1941 and 1944), 13 to Romania and 22 to Yugoslavia, where 48 more were built under licence by Ikarus. The Blenheim Mk IV was a Mk I airframe with two 995hp (742kW) Mercury XV radials driving de Havilland three-blade variable pitch propellers, extra fuel tankage and a longer nose.

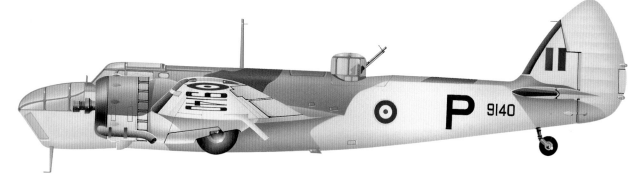

The Bristol Blenheim was used in a variety of roles. This example wears the camouflage of a maritime patrol aircraft.

Heinkel He 111

The Heinkel He 111 was designed early in 1934 by Siegfried and Walter Gunter as a high-speed transport and as a bomber for the still-secret Luftwaffe. The design owed a great deal to that of the earlier He 70.

COUNTRY OF ORIGIN: Germany

TYPE: (He 111P-2) four-seat medium bomber

POWERPLANT: two 1100hp (820kW) Daimler-Benz DB 601A-1 12-cylinder engines

PERFORMANCE: maximum speed 398km/h (247mph); climb to 4500m (14,765ft) in 31 minutes 18 seconds; service ceiling 8000m (26,245ft); range 2400km (1491 miles)

WEIGHTS: empty 8015kg (17,670lb); maximum take-off 13,500kg (29,762lb)

DIMENSIONS: span 22.60m (74ft 1.75in); length 16.40m (53ft 9.5in); height 3.4m (13ft 1.5in)

ARMAMENT: one 7.92mm fixed machine gun in the nose, one 7.92mm machine gun in the nose position, one 7.92mm machine gun in dorsal position, one 7.92mm machine gun in rear of ventral gondola, two 7.92mm machine guns in two beam positions, and provision for one 7.92mm fixed machine gun in the tail cone; bomb load of 2000kg (4409lb)

This is a Heinkel He 111 with Spanish Air Force markings. Hispano built the bomber under licence.

The Heinkel He 111 was Germany's most important medium bomber of World War II, and although ostensibly designed as a civil transport had entered air force service by 1936 as the He 111B bomber with Daimler-Benz DB 601 engines and a conventional forward fuselage with a stepped cockpit. These 300 aircraft were followed by some 190 He 111E bombers with Junkers Jumo 211 engines, and the next significant model, entering service in the spring of 1939, was the He 111P with the asymmetric fully glazed nose typical of all subsequent He 111 models.

Some 400 aircraft were built in bomber and trainer subvariants between the He 111P-1 and He 111P-6. The He 111P was a useful type whose production was curtailed only by the reallocation of DB 601 engine supplies to fighters. Many He 111P-6 aircraft were later adapted as glider tugs. Spanish aircraft makers built 236 He 111Hs under licence during and after the war as the CASA 2.111.

Mauled in the Battle of Britain

Early in World War II during operations against Poland, the losses suffered by the He 111 units were light, but it was a different story during the Battle of France, and even more so in the Battle of Britain, where they took a severe mauling. In its torpedo-bomber role, however, He 111 scored some notable successes against the Arctic convoys to Russia, notably against the ill-fated PQ17 in July 1942, when the convoy was virtually destroyed.

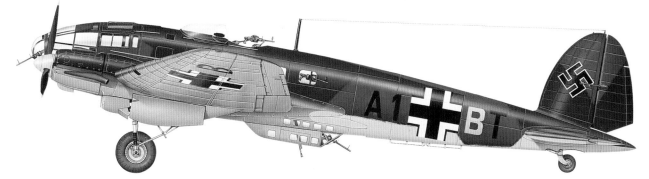

This is a Heinkel He 111P of KG53 'Legion Condor'. The He 111 was used operationally in the Spanish Civil War.

Vickers Wellesley

Designed by Barnes Wallis, who was later to design the bombs that breached the Ruhr dams in 1943, the Vickers Wellesley was a very innovative aircraft.

COUNTRY OF ORIGIN: United Kingdom

TYPE: (Wellesley Mk I) two/three-seat general-purpose bomber

POWERPLANT: one 835hp (622.5kW) Bristol Pegasus XX nine-cylinder single-row radial engine

PERFORMANCE: maximum speed 367km/h (228mph); climb to 6000m (19,685ft) in 17 minutes 30 seconds; service ceiling 7770m (25,500ft); range 4635km (2880 miles) with a 1060lb (481kg) bomb load

WEIGHTS: empty 3066kg (6760lb); maximum take-off 5670kg (12,500lb)

DIMENSIONS: span 22.73m (74ft 7in); length 11.66m (39ft 3in); height 4.67m (15ft 3.5in)

ARMAMENT: one 0.303in fixed forward-firing machine gun in the leading edge of the port wing, and one 0.303in trainable rearward-firing machine gun in the rear cockpit, plus an internal bomb load of 907kg (2000lb)

The Vickers Wellesley, seen here in pre-war markings, had a phenomenal long-range performance.

Designed in 1933 as a private venture to meet an official requirement for a general-purpose and torpedo bomber, the Wellesley was based on the novel geodetic structure, emerging for its first flight in June 1935 as a fabric-covered cantilever monoplane with a high aspect ratio wing.

Covering vast distances

The Air Ministry ordered an initial 96 Wellesley Mk I aircraft optimized for the medium bomber role with its bombs carried in two panniers under the wing. The Wellesley Mk I entered service in April 1937, and production up to May 1938 totalled 176 aircraft, most of the later aircraft being completed with a continuous 'glasshouse' canopy bridging the front and rear cockpits. The Wellesley saw useful service in East and North Africa during the first part of World War II. It also made some notable long-distance flights. On 5 November, 1938, three aircraft set off from Ismailia, Egypt, to fly to Australia. One had to land at Keopang, on Timpor in the Dutch East Indies, but the other two flew on in deteriorating weather to reach Darwin after covering a straight-line distance of 11,523km (7162 miles) in 48 hours.

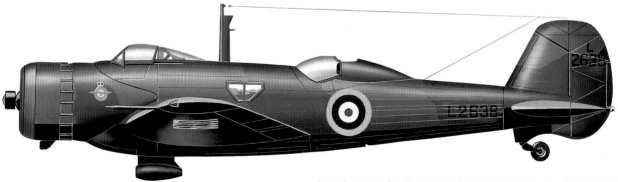

An early production Wellesley, this example shows the original tandem cockpit configuration.

Boeing B-17

The B-17 Flying Fortress took the daylight bombing battle into the heart of Germany, sustaining heavy losses until an effective fighter escort came along.

COUNTRY OF ORIGIN: USA

TYPE: (B-17F) 10-seat medium bomber

POWERPLANT: four 1200hp (895kW) Wright R-1820-97 nine-cylinder single-row radial engines

PERFORMANCE: maximum speed 523km/h (325mph); climb to 6095m (20,000ft) in 25 minutes 42 seconds; ceiling 11,430m (37,500ft); range 7113km (4420miles)

WEIGHTS: empty 16,206kg (35,728lb); maximum take-off 32,6591kg (72,000lb)

DIMENSIONS: span 31.63m (103ft 9.38in); length 22.78m (74ft 9in); height 5.85m (19ft 2.5in)

ARMAMENT: two 0.3in trainable forward-firing machine guns in cheek positions, three 0.5in trainable machine guns in dorsal positions, two 0.5in trainable machine guns in the ventral position, and one 0.5in trainable lateral-firing machine gun in each of the two waist positions, plus an internal bomb load of 4761kg (10,496lb)

The B-17 Flying Fortress carried the daylight bombing war deep into the heart of Germany.

The B-17 Flying Fortress, bearing the company designation Boeing Model 299, first flew on 28 July 1935. The first production batch of 39 B-17Bs were all delivered by the end of March 1940; meanwhile a further order had been placed for 38 B-17Cs, which were powered by four Wright 1200hp (882kW) Cyclone engines. By the time the Pacific war began, the B-17D was in service.

New tail gun position

A new tail design, the main recognition feature of all subsequent Fortresses, was introduced with the B-17E, together with improved armament which, for the first time, included a tail gun position. It was followed by the B-17F and the definitive version, the B-17G. The B-17D paved the way for the first large-scale production model of the Flying Fortress, the B-17E. Some 512 were delivered and featured a redesigned, enlarged tail unit for improved stability at high altitude, and a revised defensive scheme including a twin-gun tail position and power-operated twin-gun dorsal and ventral turrets. The B-17E entered service in 1942, and was soon supplemented by the B-17F. This was the definitive model: 3,405 aircraft were produced by three manufacturers. The B-17F introduced a frameless Plexiglas nose transparency, structural strengthening for higher-weight operations, and further refinement of the defensive armament. Small numbers of B-17E and B-17F bombers were operated by the British with the designations Fortress Mk IIA and Fortress Mk II respectively. A number were captured intact by the Germans and evaluated in Luftwaffe markings.

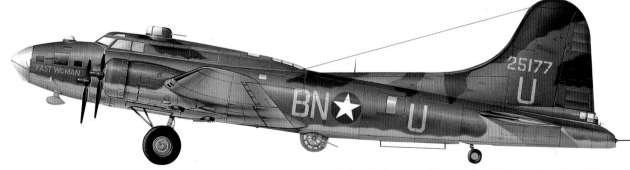

This B-17 is in the markings of the 359th Bomb Squadron, 303rd Bombardment Group, Molesworth, England, 1943.

Consolidated PBY Catalina

On 28 February, 1928, the US Navy issued a contract for a prototype flying boat, the XPY-1, to the Consolidated Aircraft Corporation. This aircraft was the first large monoplane flying boat procured by the USN.

COUNTRY OF ORIGIN: USA

TYPE: (PBY-5) nine-seat maritime reconnaissance and bomber flying boat

POWERPLANT: two 1200hp (895kW) Pratt & Whitney R-1830-82 Twin Wasp 14-cylinder two-row radial engines

PERFORMANCE: maximum speed 322km/h (200mph); maximum rate of climb 302m (990ft) per minute; ceiling 6585m (21,600ft); range 3050km (1895 miles)

WEIGHTS: empty 7893kg (17,400lb); maximum take-off 15,145kg (33,389lb)

DIMENSIONS: span 31.70m (104ft); length 19.45m (63ft 10in); height 5.76m (18ft 11in)

ARMAMENT: two 0.3in trainable forward-firing machine guns in bow turret, one 0.3in trainable rearward-firing machine gun in ventral tunnel position, and one 0.5in trainable lateral-firing machine gun in each 'blister' beam position, plus an external load of 2041kg (4500lb)

The PBY Catalina went a long way towards closing the dangerous so-called mid-Atlantic gap, where U-boats preyed on Allied convoys.

The PBY series, now known as the Catalina after its British designation, was built in larger numbers than all other flying boats combined over a period of 10 years on six production lines. The type was extremely slow, even by the standards of flying boats in World War II, but it was also extremely reliable, with good endurance.

Waist blisters not hatches
The XP3Y-1 prototype made its maiden flight in March 1934, and there followed 60, 50, 66, 33 and 1024 examples respectively of the PBY-1, improved PBY-2, PBY-3 with uprated engines, PBY-4 with further uprated engines, and PBY-5 with still more power and with waist blisters rather than hatches. It was also built in Canada as the Boeing PB2B and in the USSR. Further development of the Catalina resulted in the PBY-6A (235 aircraft) with revised armament, an enlarged tail and a search radar scanner mounted over the cockpit, and the Naval Aircraft Factory PBN-1 Nomad (156 aircraft), built to PBY-5A standard but with a larger tail unit, greater fuel capacity and better armament. Most were shipped to the USSR. Three examples of the PBY-3 were also delivered to the USSR in 1938, along with a manufacturing licence. The Soviet version, designated GST and powered by Russian-built 950hp M87 engines, was used in the transport role.

This PBY-5A is brightly coloured for its search and rescue role, a task to which it was well suited.

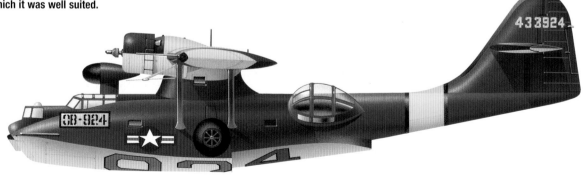

Douglas SBD Dauntless

The evolution of the Douglas SBD Dauntless began in November 1934, when a Northrop design team based a proposal for a new navy dive-bomber on the Northrop A-17, a light attack bomber about to enter production.

COUNTRY OF ORIGIN: USA

TYPE: (SBD-5) two-seat carrierborne and land-based scout and dive-bomber

POWERPLANT: one 1200hp (895kW) Wright R-1820-60 Cyclone nine-cylinder single-row radial engine

PERFORMANCE: maximum speed 410km/h (255mph); climb to 3050m (10,000ft) in 8 minutes; service ceiling 7780m (25,530ft); range 2519km (1565 miles)

WEIGHTS: empty 2905kg (6404lb); maximum take-off 4853kg (10,700lb)

DIMENSIONS: span 12.66m (41ft 6.38in); length 10.09m (33ft 1.25in); height 4.14m (13ft 7in)

ARMAMENT: two 0.5in fixed forward-firing machine guns in the upper part of the forward fuselage, and two 0.3in trainable rearward-firing machine guns in the rear of the cockpit, plus an external bomb load of 1021kg (2250lb

Dauntless aircraft take up formation over the deep blue waters of the Caribbean during a training sortie.

The Dauntless was one of World War II's decisive warplanes, particularly in terms of the part it played in the Battle of Midway, and despite the fact that it possessed only indifferent performance and poor manoeuvrability.

Battle damage absorber

As a result of these shortcomings the type was phased out of first-line service before the end of the war despite having only entered service in 1940. The attrition rate of the Dauntless squadrons, on the other hand, was the lowest of any US carrier aircraft in the Pacific, thanks to the SBD's ability to absorb an amazing amount of battle damage. Later, when they had been replaced in the dive-bombing role by the Curtiss SB2C Helldiver, they were assigned to escort carriers, carrying out anti-submarine warfare or close support missions. In the Solomons campaign, it made an enormous contribution to the eventual US victory in the battle for Guadalcanal; and it sank a greater tonnage of Japanese shipping than any other aircraft. The first prototype flight of the XBT-2 (converted Northrop BT-1) was in April 1938. The main production models were the SBD-1 (57) with the 1000hp (746kW) R-1820-32 engine, SBD-2 (87) with heavier armament and more fuel, SBD-3 (584) with 0.5in machine guns, self-sealing fuel tankage and 24-volt electrics, SBD-4 (780) with detail improvements, SBD-5 (3025) with greater power, and SBD-6 (451) with the 1350hp (1007kW) R-1820-66 engine.

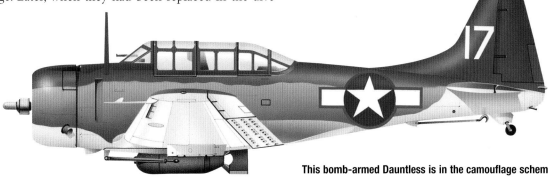

This bomb-armed Dauntless is in the camouflage scheme adopted by the US Navy soon after the outbreak of the Pacific war.

Junkers Ju 87

The word Stuka, short for *Sturzkampfflugzeug* (diving combat aircraft) was applied to all German bomber aircraft with a dive-bombing capability during World War II, but will forever be linked with the Junkers Ju 87.

COUNTRY OF ORIGIN: Germany

TYPE: (Ju 87D-1) two-seat dive-bomber and close support warplane

POWERPLANT: one 1400hp (1044kW) Junkers Jumo 211J-1 12-cylinder inverted-Vee engine

PERFORMANCE: maximum speed 410km/h (255mph); climb to 5000m (16,405ft) in 19 minutes 48 seconds; service ceiling 7300m (23,950ft); range 1535km (954 miles)

WEIGHTS: empty 3900kg (8598lb); maximum take-off 6600kg (14,550lb)

DIMENSIONS: span 13.80m (45ft 3.33in); length 11.50m (37ft 8.75in); height 3.88m (12ft 9.25in)

ARMAMENT: two 7.92mm fixed forward-firing machine guns in the leading edges of the wing and one 7.92mm trainable two-barrel rearward-firing machine gun in the rear of the cockpit, plus an external bomb load of 1800kg (3968lb)

An early-model Ju 87B Stuka in pre-war Luftwaffe camouflage.

The prototype Ju 87V1 was flown for the first time in the late spring 1935, powered by a 640hp (477kW) Rolls-Royce Kestrel engine. Production began with the pre-series Ju 87A-0, powered by the Jumo 210Da engine, and continued with the Ju 87A-1, first deliveries of which were made to I/St.G 162 Immelmann, in 1937. It was succeeded on the production line in 1938 by an extensively modified version, the Ju 87B, which used the more powerful 1100hp (820kW) Jumo 211Da. It had a redesigned cockpit and a 'spatted' undercarriage. An anti-shipping version of the Ju 87B-2 was known as the Ju

87R. By early 1940, the new Jumo 211J-1 inverted-Vee piston engine was ready, and the Junkers design team set about evolving a development of the Ju 87B to exploit this engine, which offered not only greater power but also the possibility of a considerably cleaner installation.

Redesigned cockpit

Other changes were a complete redesign of the cockpit enclosure to reduce drag, a reduction in the size and complexity of the main landing-gear fairings, an increase in the internal fuel capacity, improvement of crew protection using thicker armour, the doubling of the defensive firepower, and the strengthening of the lower fuselage and attached crutch for the ability to carry one 3968lb (1800kg) bomb. There were seven subvariants of the Ju 87D between the Ju 87D-1 and Ju 87D-8 for a variety of roles ranging from glider-towing (Ju 87D-2) to night ground attack (Ju 87D-7). The final version of the Stuka was the Ju 87G 'tank-buster'.

The 1943 Junkers Ju 87G 'tank-buster' of StG3, Russia, was armed with two 37mm cannons.

Mitsubishi G3M Nell

The Mitubshi G3M saw widespread service during the Pacific war. One of its first sucessful actions was the sinking of HM warships *Prince of Wales* and *Repulse* off Malaya on 10 December 1941.

COUNTRY OF ORIGIN: Japan

TYPE: (G3M2) seven-seat medium attack bomber

POWERPLANT: two 1075hp (801.5kW) Mitsubishi Kinsei 41,42 or 45 14-cylinder two-row radial engines

PERFORMANCE: maximum speed 373km/h (232mph); climb to 3000m (9845ft) in 8 minutes 19 seconds; service ceiling 9130m (29,950ft); range 4380km (2722 miles)

WEIGHTS: empty 4965kg (10,936lb); maximum take-off 8000kg (17,637lb)

DIMENSIONS: span 25m (82ft 0.25in); length 16.45m (53ft 11.63in); height 3.69m (12ft 1in)

ARMAMENT: one 20mm trainable rearward-firing cannon in dorsal turret, one 7.7mm trainable machine gun in retractable dorsal turret, one 7.7mm machine gun in each beam position, and provision for one 7.7mm machine gun in cockpit, plus a bomb load of 800kg (1764lb)

A Mitsubishi G3M Nell airborne for a combat mission. The under-fuselage bomb racks are clearly visible.

Already obsolescent when Japan entered World War II in 1941, the G3M belied its technical limitations by scoring stunning successes in the opening phases of Japan's offensive onslaught. The lack of an adequate replacement meant that the 'Nell' was forced to soldier on into total obsolescence and suffered devastatingly heavy losses.

Air power in the Pacific
First flown in July 1935, the G3M was designed to project the Imperial Japanese Navy Air Force's power deep into the Pacific. The G3M1 variant entered service in 1937, but these 34 aircraft were soon supplanted by an eventual 993 examples of the G3M2 and G3M3 (both with uprated engines and increased fuel capacity). The G3M was widely used in China, and about 250 were still in first-line service when Japan entered World War II. Some specially converted aircraft were used to photograph US installations in the Pacific before the attack on Pearl Harbor. The G3M had excellent range, which enabled it to travel far and wide over mainland China and Southeast Asia, its principal areas of operations. Some aircraft were also converted as L3Y armed transport aircraft.

The Mitsubishi G3M's very long range was an enormous asset to the Imperial Japanese Navy in its early Pacific offensives.

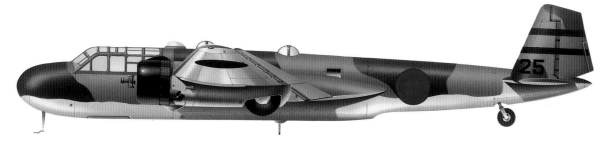

Armstrong Whitworth Whitley

Together with the Vickers Wellington and Handley Page Hampden, the Armstrong Whitworth Whitley sustained RAF Bomber Command's strategic bombing offensive during the early part of World War II.

The Armstrong Whitworth Whitley had a long range and, in addition to its primary bombing role, was used for dropping agents.

COUNTRY OF ORIGIN: United Kingdom

TYPE: (Whitley Mk V) five-man long-range night bomber

POWERPLANT: two 1145hp (854kW) Rolls-Royce Merlin X 12-cylinder Vee engines

PERFORMANCE: maximum speed 370km/h (230mph); climb to 4570m (15,000ft) in 16 minutes 0 seconds; service ceiling 7925m (26,000ft); range 2655km (1650 miles) with standard fuel and a 1361kg (3000lb) bomb load

WEIGHTS: empty 8777kg (19,350lb); maximum take-off 15,195kg (33,500lb)

DIMENSIONS: span 25.60m (84ft 0in); length 21.49m (70ft 6in); height 4.57m (15ft 0in)

ARMAMENT: one 0.303in trainable forward-firing machine gun in the nose turret, and four 0.303in trainable rearward-firing machine guns in the tail turret, plus an internal bomb load of 7000lb (3175kg)

Obsolescent at the beginning of World War II, the Whitley was still one of Bomber Command's mainstays in 1939. In the early days of the war it was a night bomber before passing to Coastal Command as a patrol and anti-submarine type and finishing up as a glider-towing and paratroop training machine. The Whitley Mk I (34 aircraft) entered service in March 1937 with Armstrong Siddeley Tiger radial engines, which were retained in the 126 improved Mk II and Mk III aircraft, while the 33 Whitley Mk IV bombers switched to Rolls-Royce Merlin engines and introduced a powered tail turret.

Long-range missions

The main variant, the Mk V, had a longer rear fuselage, revised tail unit and greater fuel capacity. These 1,466 aircraft were followed by the 146 Mk VII for Coastal Command with air-to-surface search radar. They carried out some notable long-range missions, including the first raid on Italy in June 1940. They were also used for special operations, such as dropping paratroops and agents. For example, in February 1942, Whitleys of No 51 Squadron dropped a force of paratroops at Bruneval, north of Le Havre, to seize components of an enemy radar station.

The Whitley illustrated here carries the code letters of No. 26 Operational Training Unit.

Fairey Battle

The Fairey Battle single-engined light bomber, one of the types chosen for large-scale production, first flew in March 1936, the first deliveries being made to No. 63 Squadron in May 1937.

COUNTRY OF ORIGIN: United Kingdom

TYPE: (Battle Mk II) two/three-seat light day bomber

POWERPLANT: one 1030hp (768kW) Rolls-Royce Merlin II 12-cylinder Vee engine

PERFORMANCE: maximum speed 406km/h (252mph); climb to 4570m (15,000ft) in 16 minutes 12 seconds; service ceiling 7925m (26,000ft); range 1931km (1200 miles) with a 644kg (1420lb) bomb load

WEIGHTS: empty 3361kg (7410lb); normal take-off 4944kg (10,900lb); maximum take-off 5307kg (11,700lb)

DIMENSIONS: Span 16.45m (54ft); length 12.93m (42ft 5in); height 4.57m (15ft)

ARMAMENT: one 0.303in fixed forward-firing machine gun in the leading edge of the starboard wing, and one 0.303in trainable rearward-firing machine gun in the rear cockpit, plus an internal and external bomb load of 680kg (1500lb)

The Fairey Battle light bomber was under-armed and underpowered and suffered terrible casualties in the Battle of France.

The Battle was an advance over the Hawker light bomber biplanes that it was designed to replace in Royal Air Force service. Yet it was technically and tactically obsolescent by the time it entered service in March 1937, as a result of the rapid pace of aeronautical development during the approach to World War II. This is unsurprising as the plane was designed to meet a 1932 requirement but did not fly until March 1936. Production of the Battle light bomber totalled 1818 from two British manufacturers for RAF service (subsequently redesignated as the Battle Mks I to V depending on the mark of engine installed) and 18 Belgian-built aircraft for Belgian service.

Appalling losses

It was relegated to second-line service in 1940 as the Battle (T) trainer and Battle (TT) target-tug. In September 1939 ten Battle squadrons of the Advanced Air Striking Force deployed to France. In May 1940 they suffered appalling losses attempting to bomb enemy columns and bridges over the Meuse. In the first five days of the Battle of France the Fairey Battle squadrons lost 86 aircraft.

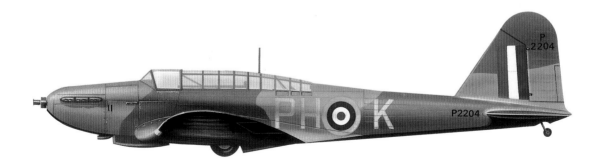

A Fairey Battle seen in the markings of No. 12 Squadron RAF, which carried out a suicidal attack on the Meuse bridges on 12 May 1940.

Ilyushin Il-4

The most widely used Soviet bomber of WWII, the Ilyushin Il-4 was designed in 1936 as the TsKB-26 and given the military designation DB-3, the letters denoting *Dalnii Bombardirovchtchik* (long-range bomber).

COUNTRY OF ORIGIN: USSR

TYPE: four-seat long-range medium bomber

POWERPLANT: two 1100hp (820kW) Tumanskii M-88B 14-cylinder two-row radial engine

PERFORMANCE: maximum speed 420km/h (261mph); climb to 5000m (16,405ft) in 12 minutes; service ceiling 9400m (30,840ft); ran(1616 miles) with a 1000kg (2205lb) bomb load

WEIGHTS: empty 5800kg (12,787lb); maximum take-off 10,300kg (22,707lb)

DIMENSIONS: span 21.44m (70ft 4.5in); length 14.80m (48ft 7in); height 4.10m (13ft 5.5in)

ARMAMENT: one 7.62mm trainable forward-firing machine gun in nose position, one 7.62mm trainable machine gun in dorsal turret, and one 7.62mm trainable rearward-firing machine gun in ventral hatch position, plus an internal bomb load of 2700kg (5952lb)

Designed as the DB-3f and first flown in January 1940 for service from 1941, the Il-4 was a modernized version of the DB-3M. The Il-4 remained in production up to 1944 and with a total of 5256 aircraft was among the Soviets' most important medium bombers of World War II. The first aircraft were powered by two 1000hp (746kW) Tumanskii M-88 radial engines, but these were soon replaced by uprated versions of the same engine.

Shown here is an Illyushin Il-4 (DB-3F) of a Red Air Force *bombardirovoishchnaya aviatsionyyl* **polk (bomber regiment) in 1944.**

The Il-4 was the first Soviet heavy bomber to attack Berlin, and was used operationally throughout the war.

Adding extra crew

Other changes included during the production run included a four- rather than three-man crew, self-sealing fuel tanks, and larger-calibre defensive weapons: the 7.62mm turret gun was replaced by a 12.7mm machine gun and then a 20mm cannon, and the machine gun in the nose was changed to a 20mm cannon. The Il-4 was used extensively by both the Soviet Air Force and Soviet Navy; on the night of 8/9 August 1941 it carried out the Soviet AF's first attack on Berlin, and continued to carry out similar attacks at intervals for the duration of the war. It also operated during the Soviet-Finnish Winter War of 1939-40, where it suffered heavy losses because of its inadequate defensive firepower.

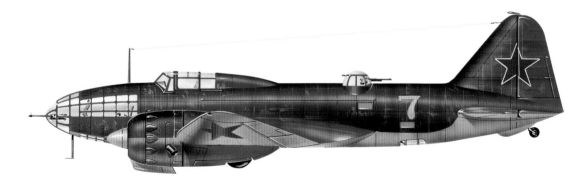

Fiat BR.20 Cicogna

Designed by Celestino Rosatelli, the Fiat BR.20 medium bomber was modern and technically advanced when the prototype flew in February 1936, but it was already obsolescent by the time Italy entered World War II in 1940.

COUNTRY OF ORIGIN: Italy

TYPE: (BR.20M) five-seat medium bomber

POWERPLANT: two 1030hp (768kW) Fiat A.80 RC.41 14-cylinder two-row radial engines

PERFORMANCE: maximum speed 430km/h (267mph); climb to 5000m (16,405ft) in 17 minutes 56 seconds; service ceiling 7200m (23,620ft); range 1240km (770.5 miles) with a 1000kg (2205lb) bomb load

WEIGHTS: empty 6740kg (14,859lb); maximum take-off 10,340kg (22,795lb)

DIMENSIONS: span 21.56m (70ft 8.8in); length 16.17m (53ft 0.5in); height 4.30m (14ft 1.25in)

ARMAMENT: one 7.7mm trainable forward-firing machine gun in the nose turret, two 7.7mm or one 12.7mm trainable rearward-firing machine guns in the dorsal turret, and one 7.7mm trainable machine gun in the ventral hatch position, plus an internal bomb load of 1600kg (3527lb)

The Fiat BR.20 saw service on all fronts during World War II and was exported to several countries, including Japan.

The BR.20 Cicogna ('Stork') was the first 'modern' medium bomber produced in Italy during the lead-up to World War II, and first flew in prototype form during February 1936 for service from the autumn of the same year. Delivery of 320 aircraft, including 85 for Japan and one for Venezuela, was followed by production of 264 improved BR.20M bombers.

Heavy losses

This model had improved nose contours, revised armament and increased armour protection. The final variant was the BR.20bis (15 aircraft) with two 1250hp (932kW) Fiat A.82 RC.42S radial engines, two 7.7mm machine guns in waist positions, and a power-operated dorsal turret. Over 160 Cicogna bombers were available when Italy entered World War II. Most were lost in operations before Italy's September 1943 armistice with the Allies. Some BR.20s were delivered to Japan, which used the aircraft as an interim bomber during its operations in Manchuria. About half the total production involved the BR.20M, an improved model with better streamlining, heavier defensive armament and more armour. The BR.20 was used in the Spanish Civil War and saw service on all fronts in WWII, taking part in night attacks on the British Isles in October and November 1940. It was used extensively against Malta in the early months of the Axis offensive.

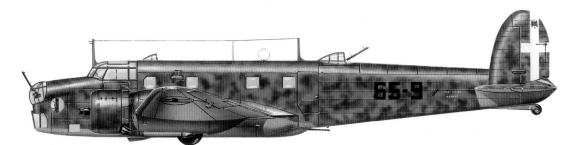

A Fiat BR.20 of the 65th Squadriglia, which served in Italy's Balkan campaign of 1940.

Vickers Wellington

The Vickers Wellington featured geodetic construction, a 'basket weave' construction system producing a self-stabilizing framework members in which loads in any direction were automatically equalized.

A Vickers Wellington Mk III bearing the code letters of No. 419 Squadron RCAF, Middleton St George, County Durham.

COUNTRY OF ORIGIN: United Kingdom

TYPE: (Wellington Mk X) six-seat medium bomber

POWERPLANT: two 1675hp (1249kW) Bristol Hercules XI or XVI 14-cylinder two-row radial engines

PERFORMANCE: maximum speed 410km/h (255mph); climb to 4570m (15,000ft) in 27 minutes 42 seconds; service ceiling 6705m (22,000ft); range 3033.5km (1885 miles) with a 680kg (1500lb) bomb load

WEIGHTS: empty 10,194kg (22,474lb); maximum take-off 16,556kg (36,500lb)

DIMENSIONS: span 26.26m (86ft 2in); length 19.68m (64ft 7in); height 5.31m (17ft 5in)

ARMAMENT: two 0.303in trainable forward-firing machine guns in nose turret, four 0.303in trainable rearward-firing machine guns in tail turret, and one 0.303in trainable lateral-firing machine gun in each beam position, plus an internal bomb load of 2041kg (4500lb)

One of the most important warplanes in the British inventory at the beginning of World War II, the Wellington bore the brunt of the bomber effort until large numbers of four-engined heavy bombers became available late in 1941. The type then found an important second career in the maritime reconnaissance, transport and training roles until a time well after the end of the war.

'Thousand-bomber' raid

Total production was 11,461, the last machine not being delivered until October 1945. Entering service in October 1938, the initial model was the Wellington Mk I with 1000hp (746kW) Pegasus XVIII engines. Development continued via the Mk III with Rolls-Royce Merlin Vee engines, Mk III with Hercules radial engines, Mk IV with Pratt & Whitney Twin Wasp radial engines, Mk VI with

Merlin engines, and Mk X with Hercules engines. The Wellington III entered service with No. 9 Squadron in June 1941, and underpinned Bomber Command's night offensive against Germany until the Command's four-engined heavy bombers became available in numbers. On the night of 30/31 May 1942, when 1042 aircraft set out for Cologne on what was to be Bomber Command's first 'thousand-bomber' raid, the force included 599 Wellingtons. Coastal Command also used 271 Wellington GR.IIIs as general reconnaissance versions of the aircraft, fitted with ASV Mk II radar and carrying torpedoes.

A Vickers Wellington Mk 1 of No 99 Squadron, Newmarket, 1940.

Junkers Ju 88

One of the most versatile and effective combat aircraft ever produced, the Junkers Ju 88 remained of vital importance to the Luftwaffe throughout World War II, serving in a multitude of roles.

COUNTRY OF ORIGIN: Germany

TYPE: (Ju 88A-4) four-seat high-speed, level and dive-bomber

POWERPLANT: two 1340hp (999kW) Junkers Jumo 211J-1/2 12-cylinder engines

PERFORMANCE: Maximum speed 470km/h (292mph); climb to 5400m (17,715ft) in 23 minutes; service ceiling 26,900ft (8200m); range 2730km (1696 miles)

WEIGHTS: empty 9860kg (21,737lb); maximum take-off 14,000kg (30,865lb)

DIMENSIONS: Span 20.00m (65ft 7.5in); length 14.40m (47ft 2.75in); height 4.85m (15ft 11in)

ARMAMENT: one 7.92mm fixed or trainable forward-firing machine gun in windscreen, one 13mm or two 7.92mm forward-firing machine guns in nose position, two 7.92mm machine guns in rear of cockpit, and one 13mm or two 7.92mm trainable rearward-firing machine guns in rear of undernose gondola, plus a bomb load of 2500kg (5511lb).

A Ju 88 runs up its engines prior to a flight test. The Ju 88 was one of the classic aircraft of all time.

Rivalling the Mosquito as the most versatile warplane of World War II, the Ju 88 was schemed as a high-speed level and dive bomber and first flew in December 1936 for entry into service during 1939. The most important early model was the Ju 88A, of which over 7000 were delivered in variants up to the Ju 88A-17.

Service in the Arctic
The Ju 88A-4 served in both Europe and North Africa and incorporated improvements resulting from the combat experience gained during the battles of France and Britain. Twenty Ju 88A-4s were supplied to Finland,

and some were supplied to Italy, Romania and Hungary. The Ju 88A-5 was generally similar, with some equipment changes. The Ju 88A saw considerable action in the Balkans and the Mediterranean, and on the Eastern Front. Some of their most outstanding service, however, was in the Arctic, where aircraft of KG 26 and KG 30, based in northern Norway, carried out devastating attacks on Allied convoys to Russia. The Ju 88D was a long-range reconnaissance development of which some 1450 were delivered. The Ju 88H was another reconnaissance model of which small numbers were completed with 1700hp (1267.5kW) BMW 801 radial engines, and the Ju 88S was a high-speed bomber of which modest numbers were produced with radial or Vee engines. The Ju 88T was a reconnaissance derivative of the Ju 88S. The final total of 15,000 Ju 88s of all models gives an idea of the significance of this aircraft.

This is a Junkers Ju 88A of KG30, Denmark, 1940. The unit later moved to Norway.

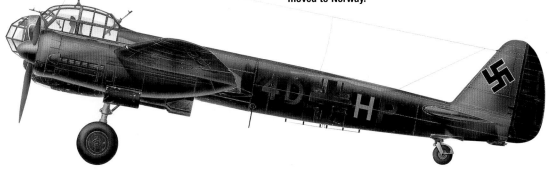

Mitsubishi Ki 21 'Sally'

The Mitsubishi Ki.21 (Army Type 97) heavy bomber first flew on 18 December 1936, and when deliveries to the JAAF began in August 1938 it had few equals anywhere in the world.

COUNTRY OF ORIGIN: Japan

TYPE: (Ki-21-IIb) five/seven-seat 'heavy' (actually medium) bomber

POWERPLANT: two 1500hp (1118kW) Mitsubishi Ha-101 (Army Type 100) 14- cylinder two-row radial engines; maximum speed 486km/h (302mph); climb to 6000m (19,685ft) in 13 minutes 13 seconds; service ceiling 10,000m (32,810ft); range 2700km (1678 miles)

WEIGHTS: empty 6070kg (13,382lb); maximum take-off 10,610kg (23,391lb)

DIMENSIONS: span 22.50m (73ft 9.75in); length 16.00m (52ft 6in); height 4.85m (15ft 11in)

ARMAMENT: one 12.7mm trainable machine gun in dorsal turret, one 7.7mm machine gun in nose position, one 7.7mm machine gun in ventral position, one 7.7mm machine gun in tail position, and one 7.7mm machine gun in each beam position; bomb load of 1000kg (2205lb)

The Ki.27 'Sally' saw much action with the Imperial Japanese Army Air Force, both in China and the Pacific.

The best bomber that was available in numbers to the Imperial Japanese Army Air Force in World War II, the Ki-21 was another example of Japan's short-sighted policy of insisting on high speed and long range by sacrificing protection, defensive firepower and offensive warload.

Powerful but defenceless

The first of eight prototypes made their maiden flight in December 1936. The Ki-21 entered service in mid-1938; production totalled 774 examples of the Ki-21-I with 850hp (634kW) Nakajima Ha-5 radial engines in three subvariants, and 1278 examples of the Ki-21-II with a different and uprated powerplant in two subvariants. Some Ki-21-Is were converted as MC-21 unarmed civil transports. The first production model, the Ki.21-I, was in service from the beginning of the Sino-Japanese conflict of 1939 until the end of the Pacific war, and served at the forefront of the Japanese attacks on Hong Kong, Thailand, the Philippines, Malaya, the Dutch East Indies and Burma, where it suffered badly in the face of determined fighter opposition because of its inadequate defensive armament and lack of armour.

This is a Ki-21-IIb of the Imperial Japanese Army air service, as it appeared in 1944.

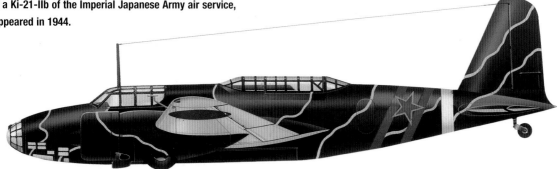

CANT Z.1007 Alcione

The CANT Z.1107 was widely used by the Regia Aeronautica throughout the Balkans and the Mediterranean. The aircraft was produced in both single-and twin-finned configurations.

The Cant Z.1007 was an excellent high-level bomber, and its crews became quite famous for their level of accuracy.

COUNTRY OF ORIGIN: Italy

TYPE: (Z.1007bis) five-seat medium bomber

POWERPLANT: three 1000hp (746kW) Piaggio P.XI R2C.40 14-cylinder two-row radial engines

PERFORMANCE: maximum speed 466km/h (290mph); climb to 4000m (13,125ft) in 10 minutes 30 seconds; service ceiling 8200m (26,900ft); range 1750km (1087 miles) with a 1200kg (2646lb) bomb load

WEIGHTS: empty 9396kg (20,715lb); maximum take-off 13,621kg (30,029lb)

DIMENSIONS: span 24.80m (81ft 4.33in); length 18.35mn (60ft 2.5in); height 5.22m (17ft 5in)

ARMAMENT: one 12.7mm trainable machine gun in the dorsal turret, one 12.7mm trainable rearward-firing machine gun in the ventral step position, and one 7.7mm lateral-firing machine gun in each of the two beam positions, internal bomb load of 1200kg (2646lb)

First flown in prototype form during March 1937, the Z.1007 Alcione ('Kingfisher') entered service late in 1938 and became one of Italy's most important medium bombers. Production of the Z.1007 totalled 35 aircraft with 840hp (626kW) Piaggio Asso XI radial engines and four 7.7mm machine guns. This was followed by 526 examples of the Z.1007bis and Z.1007ter. The former introduced a larger airframe, an uprated powerplant with engines in revised nacelles, and different armament as well as two types of tail unit (single vertical surface in first three batches and twin surfaces in the last six batches). The latter had the uprated powerplant of three 1175hp (876kW)

Piaggio P.XIX radial engines but a reduced 1000kg (2205lb) bomb load.

Attacking Malta

The Z.1107 was widely used by the Regia Aeronautica throughout the Balkans and the Mediterranean. It saw extensive use in the air attacks on the island of Malta, from 1940-42. A twin-engined development, the potentially excellent CANT Z.1008, never went into production. The Z.1007 fought on both sides, some being taken over after the Armistice by the Italian Co-Belligerent Air Force and its rival, the National Republican Aviation.

A Cant Z.1007bis of the 172nd Squadriglia. The bomber first played a major role in the Greek campaign.

Liore et Olivier LeO 451

The LeO was without doubt the finest bomber to serve with the Armee de l'Air before France's collapse in June 1940. Production had been stepped up too late.

COUNTRY OF ORIGIN: France

TYPE: (LeO 451B.4) four-seat medium bomber

POWERPLANT: two 1140hp (850kW) Gnome-Rhône 14N-48/49 14-cylinder two-row radial engines

PERFORMANCE: maximum speed 495km/h (307mph); climb to 5000m (16,405ft) in 14 minutes; service ceiling 9000m (29,530ft); range 2300km (1429 miles) with a 500kg (1102lb) bomb load

WEIGHTS: empty 7815kg (17,229lb); normal take-off 11,400kg (25,133lb)

DIMENSIONS: span 22.52m (73ft 10.5in); length 17.17m (56ft 4in); heght 5.24m (17ft 2.25in)

ARMAMENT: one 7.5mm fixed forward-firing machine gun in the forward fuselage, one 20mm rearward-firing cannon in the dorsal turret, and one 7.5mm machine gun in the ventral turret, plus an external bomb load of 2000kg (4409lb)

The LeO 451 was a fine bomber, but in the Battle of France it was forced to operate in skies dominated by enemy fighters.

The finest bomber developed by the French aero industry before World War II, the LeO 451 confirmed that French designers had finally abandoned the angular, slab-sided machines that had trundled throughout the skies of France during most of the 1930s.

Rapid production but too late

The first of two LeO 45.01 prototypes made its maiden flight in January 1937, followed by the LeO 451B.4 production model, which entered service in the autumn of 1939. Production was rapid, and about 580 aircraft were delivered. The survivors continued in service after the fall of France, some being converted as 12-passenger civil and 17-passenger military transports, with a few remaining in service into the mid-1950s. Seven groups were equipped or partially equipped with the type during the Battle of France, in which about 130 LeO 451s were lost from all causes. At the armistice 183 LeO 451s remained in southern France and about 100 in North Africa. Some were used against Allied forces during the Syrian campaign in the summer of 1941 and others were used as transports and navigational trainers by the Luftwaffe.

The example shown here was on the strength of GB1/11 at Oran-La-Sénia (Morocco).

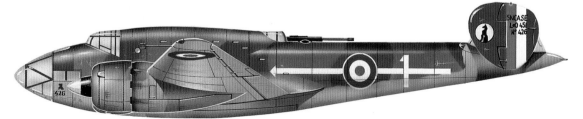

Heinkel He 115

During World War Two, the British used some captured examples of the He 115 floatplane for clandestine operations in the Mediterranean and elsewhere.

COUNTRY OF ORIGIN: Germany

TYPE: (He 115B-1) three-seat coastal general-purpose and torpedo bomber floatplane

POWERPLANT: two 960hp (716kW) BMW 132K nine-cylinder single-row radial engines

PERFORMANCE: maximum speed 295km/h (183mph); service ceiling 5200m (17,600ft); range 2600km (1616 miles)

WEIGHTS: empty 6715kg (14,804lb); normal take-off 10,400kg (22,930lb)

DIMENSIONS: span 22.28m (73ft 1in); length 17.30m (56ft 9.25in); height 6.59m (21ft 7.75in)

ARMAMENT: one 7.92mm trainable forward-firing machine gun in the nose position, and one 7.92mm trainable rearward-firing machine gun in the dorsal position, plus an internal and external torpedo, bomb and mine load of 920kg (2028lb)

The He 115 was a very effective aircraft, performing well in both torpedo-bomber and minelaying roles.

Resulting from a 1935 requirement for an advanced torpedo bomber floatplane that was also to be capable of undertaking a number of other coastal roles, such as minelaying and reconnaissance, the He 115 V1 (first of four prototypes) made its maiden flight in August 1937.

Laying mines in the North Sea

The He 115 was ordered into production early in 1938. Some 10 He 115A-0 pre-production aircraft were delivered from the summer of that year, paving the way for 137 production machines. The first of these was the baseline He 115A, and this was followed by the structurally strengthened He 115B. This in turn was operated in two main versions that spawned a number of minor subvariants for the torpedo, bombing, minelaying and reconnaissance roles. Many of these were built under licence by Weser Flugzeugbau. The He 115 was extremely active in the North Sea area during the early months of World War II, particularly in its minelaying role. Variants of the basic design were the He 115C-1, which had a heavy 15mm (0.59in) machine gun installed in the nose position; the He 115C-2, which had strengthened floats; the He 115C-3 minelayer; and the He 115C-4, equipped for Arctic operations. The final variant was the He 115E-1. During the course of its career the aircraft served with Germany, Britain and Sweden.

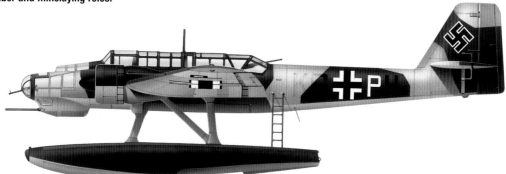

This He 115 carries the symbols of two Allied ships destroyed on its tail fin, just above the tailplane.

Short Sunderland

The design of the Short Sunderland, which was to become one of the RAF's longest-serving operational aircraft, was based on that of the stately Short C Class 'Empire' flying boats, operated by Imperial Airways in the 1930s.

COUNTRY OF ORIGIN: United Kingdom

TYPE: 10-seat maritime reconnaissance flying-boat

POWERPLANT: four 1065hp (794kW) Bristol Pegasus XVII 9-cylinder, single-row radial engines

PERFORMANCE: maximum speed 336km/h (209mph); service ceiling 4570m (15,000ft); range 4023km (2500 miles)

WEIGHTS: empty 13,875kg (30,589lb); maximum take-off 22,226kg (49,000lb)

DIMENSIONS: span 34.38m (112ft 9in); length 26m (85ft 3in); height 10.52m (34ft 6in)

ARMAMENT: two 0.303in trainable forward-firing machine guns in bow turret; two 0.303in trainable forward-firing machine guns in dorsal turret; trainable rearward-firing machine guns in tail turret; internal bomb, depth charge and mine load of 2000lb (907kg)

A 1933 requirement for a modern four-engined monoplane flying boat prompted designs from two companies including Short, which had an ideal starting point for its S.25 in the S.23 'Empire' class of civil flying boats. This proven lineage was a factor that contributed to the Air Ministry's order for 21 production examples of the S.25 in March 1936, some 18 months before the first prototype made its maiden flight in October 1937.

Major production model

The initial production model was the Sunderland MkI that entered service in the summer of 1938. When World War II started in September 1939, another two British-based squadrons had converted on to the type, and the rising rate of production allowed another three to convert during the first months of the war. Sunderland Mk I

A Short Sunderland Mk V of the Royal New Zealand Air Force kicks up a cloud of spray while taxiing.

production totalled 90 boats, 15 of them by the Blackburn Aircraft Company, all powered by 1010hp (753kW) Bristol Pegasus engines. First flown in June 1942, the Sunderland Mk III was the first major production model of the family and was in essence a late-production Sunderland Mk II with a revised planing bottom. Production of the 407 Mk IIIs lasted to late 1943. The Mk III was also converted to a long-range passenger aircraft, used by British Overseas Airways Corporation from March 1943 on gradually extending routes. Operating alongside radar-equipped Catalinas, the RAF Short Sunderlands were extremely active in hunting for U-boats over the North Atlantic. When the latter had Metox passive receivers tuned to ASV Mk II they received ample warning of the presence of British aircraft and kills plummeted. In response the RAF introduced the ASV Mk III, operating in the radar band well below 50cm (20in). When equipped in this way the Sunderland became a Mk IIIa, of which 54 were built. The last version of the Sunderland was the Mk V.

This is a Sunderland Mk III of No. 330 Squadron. This unit, manned by Norwegian personnel, was based at Sullom Voe in the Shetlands 1943–45.

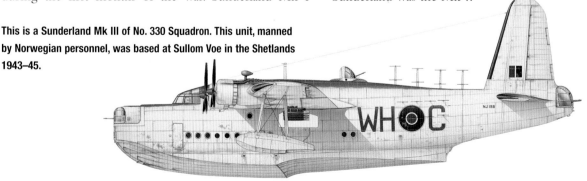

Focke-Wulf Fw 200 Condor

Normal endurance of the Condor was nine hours and 45 minutes, but with internal long-range tanks fitted the aircraft could remain airborne for as long as 18 hours.

COUNTRY OF ORIGIN: Germany

TYPE: (Fw 200C-3/U4) six-seat maritime reconnaissance bomber

POWERPLANT: four 1200hp (895kW) BMW-Bramo 323R-2 Fafnir nine-cylinder single-row radial engines

PERFORMANCE: maximum speed 360km/h (224mph); service ceiling 6000m (19,685ft); range 4440km (2759 miles)

WEIGHTS: empty 12,950kg (28,549lb); maximum take-off 22,700kg (50,044lb)

DIMENSIONS: span 32.84m (107ft 8in); length 23.46m (76ft 11.5in); height 6.30m (20ft 8in)

ARMAMENT: one 20mm trainable cannon in forward ventral gondola position, one 13mm trainable machine gun in rear dorsal position, one 13mm trainable machine gun in each beam position, one 7.92mm machine gun in rear ventral position, and one 7.92mm machine gun in forward dorsal turret, plus a bomb load of 2100kg (4630lb)

The Fw 200 Condor was an excellent long-range aircraft, but suffered from a weak structure.

The Condor is best remembered as the long-range reconnaissance aeroplane that searched for Allied convoys in the North Atlantic during World War II and then either attacked them directly with bombs/missiles or vectored-in packs of German U-boats. The type was designed as a transatlantic airliner, and first flew during July 1937.

Serious threat to Allied shipping

The first of 259 Fw 200C military aircraft entered service in September 1939. A few of these aircraft were used as VIP transports, but the majority of the machines were long-range reconnaissance bombers in seven subvariants. KG 40's Condors presented a far more serious threat than submarines to Allied shipping in the Atlantic and North Sea in 1940-41. Between August 1940 and February 1941 they claimed 368,826 tonnes (363,000 tons) sunk; most of this loss occurred in April 1941, when 116 ships totalling 328,185 tonnes (323,000 tons) were sunk. The final operational version of the Condor was the FW 200C-6, developed from the C-3 to carry a Henschel Hs 293B air-to-surface missile under each outer engine nacelle, the underwing bomb racks being removed. The combination of Hs 293 and FW 200 was first used operationally on 28 December 1943.

This Fw 200C-6 is armed with the Henschel Hs 293 anti-ship missile.

Nakajima B5N Kate

Designed in 1936, the prototype B5N torpedo-bomber first flew in January 1937 and became operational as the B5N1 light bomber in China, where it saw much operational service.

COUNTRY OF ORIGIN: Japan

TYPE: (B5N2) three-seat carrierborne and land-based torpedo and level bomber

POWERPLANT: one 1000hp (746kW) Nakajima NK1B Sakae 11 nine-cylinder single-row radial engine

PERFORMANCE: maximum speed 378km/h (235mph); climb to 3000m (9845ft) in 7 minutes 40 seconds; service ceiling 8260m (27,100ft); range 1991km (1237 miles)

WEIGHTS: empty 2279kg (5024lb); maximum take-off 4100kg (9039lb)

DIMENSIONS: span 15.52 m (50ft 11in); length 10.30m (33ft 9.5in); height 3.70m (12ft 1.75in)

ARMAMENT: one 7.7mm trainable rearward-firing machine gun in the rear cockpit, plus an external torpedo and bomb load of 800kg (1764lb)

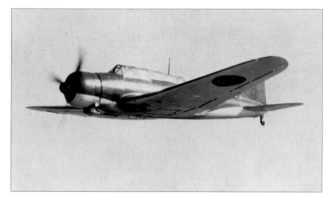

The B5N 'Kate' played a major part in securing Japan's early victories at sea in World War II.

The B5N was the torpedo and level bomber counterpart of the Aichi D3A dive-bomber, and was a major weapon in the first part of the Japanese campaign in the Pacific theatre from December 1941. The type resulted from a 1934 requirement, and the first of two prototypes flew in January 1937. Successful development paved the way for the B5N1 initial production model with the powerplant of one 840hp (626kW) Nakajima Hikari 3 radial engine.

Pearl Harbor attacker

Production of the B5N1 bomber was complemented by that of its B5N1-K advanced trainer derivative, and by 1941 the type had been replaced in first-line service by the improved B5N2 with a more potent engine. B5N production totalled 1147, and the B5N2 remained in first-line service up to mid-1944. The B5N2 featured prominently in the attack on Pearl Harbor, 144 aircraft taking part in the strike, and in the year that followed B5N2s delivered fatal blows to the US aircraft carriers *Lexington*, *Yorktown* and *Hornet*, as well as supporting Japanese amphibious assaults. The B5N2 remained in production until 1943. Many B5Ns were later assigned to anti-submarine patrol work.

Shown here is a B5N2 of the Imperial Japanese Navy Air Force, based on the ill-fated carrier *Akagi* in 1941–42.

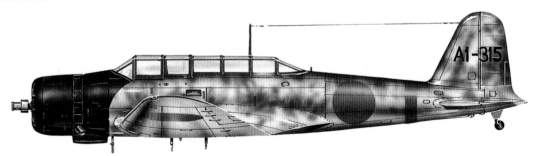

Handley Page Hampden

The Handley Page Hampden was seriously under-armed and suffered badly at the hands of enemy fighters in the early months of World War II.

One of the most important medium bombers available to the British at the start of World War II, the Hampden was in many ways a good warplane but was hampered by its narrow fuselage, which prevented crew members from taking over the task of another should he be injured. The Hampden prototype first flew in June 1937, and deliveries of the Hampden Mk I started in September 1938. Deliveries of this model amounted to 1,430 aircraft from two British and one Canadian manufacturers, the last contributing 160 machines. Another 100 Hereford craft were available for training purposes.

A Hampden of No. 455 Squadron RAAF, which transferred from Bomber to Coastal Command in 1942.

Manoevrable and daring

Nine Herefords were converted to Hampden standard, and from 1942 some 141 surviving Hampden bombers were adapted as Hampden TB.Mk I torpedo bombers for the anti-shipping role. Despite its shortcomings, the Hampden was very manoeuvrable and carried out some notable operations in the first two years of the war. One of the most outstanding was flown by Hampdens of No. 49 Squadron on the night of 12 August 1940, when the Dortmund-Ems Canal was breached in a daring low-level night attack through very heavy flak. The leader of the raid, Squadron Leader. R.A.B. Learoyd, was awarded the Victoria Cross.

COUNTRY OF ORIGIN: United Kingdom

TYPE: (Hampden Mk I) four-seat medium bomber

POWERPLANT: two 1000hp (746kW) Bristol Pegasus XVIII nine-cylinder single-row radial engines

PERFORMANCE: maximum speed 426km/h (255mph); climb to 4570m (15,000ft) in 18 minutes 54 seconds; service ceiling 6920m (22,700ft); range 3034km (1885 miles) with a 907kg (2000lb) bomb load

WEIGHTS: empty 5343kg (11,780lb); maximum take-off 10,206kg (22,500lb)

DIMENSIONS: span 21.08 m (69ft 2in); length 16.33m (53ft 7in); height 4.55m (14ft 11in)

ARMAMENT: one 0.303in fixed forward-firing machine gun in port side of the forward fuselage, one 0.303in forward-firing machine gun in nose position, two 0.303in machine guns in dorsal position, two 0.303in machine guns in ventral position; bomb load of 1814kg (4000lb)

The Hampden seen here served with No. 489 Squadron RNZAF, a torpedo-bomber unit, in 1942.

Aichi D3A Val

The Aicho D3A, featured prominently in the attack on Pearl Harbor and the Japanese conquests in South East Asia. It first flew in January 1938 and between December 1939 and August 1945, 1495 were built in two variants.

COUNTRY OF ORIGIN: Japan

TYPE: (D3A2) two-seat carrierborne and land-based dive-bomber

POWERPLANT: one 1300hp (969kW) Mitsubishi Kinsei 54 14-cylinder two-row radial engine

PERFORMANCE: maximum speed 430km/h (267mph); climb to 3000m (9845ft) in 5 minutes 48 seconds; service ceiling 10,500m (34,450ft); range 1352km (840 miles)

WEIGHTS: empty 2570kg (5666lb); maximum take-off 4122kg (9100lb)

DIMENSIONS: span 14.37m (47ft 2in); length 10.20m (33ft 5.4in); height 3.8m (12ft 7.5in)

ARMAMENT: two 7.7mm fixed forward-firing machine guns in the upper part of the forward fuselage, and one 7.7mm trainable rearward-firing machine gun in the rear cockpit, plus an external bomb load of 370kg (816lb)

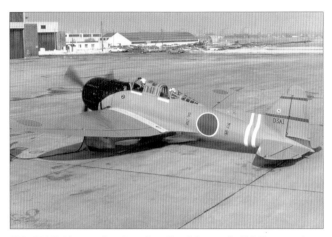

This D3A Val is a replica, based on the airframe of a T-6 Texan and produced for the film *Tora! Tora! Tora!*

The D3A is best remembered as one of the two main attack types involved in the Japanese attack on Pearl Harbor in December 1941.

Japanese mainstay

The first of eight prototype and service trials aircraft flew in January 1938, and there followed production of 470 D3A1 aircraft with the 1000hp (746kW) Mitsubishi Kinsei 43 or 1070hp (898kW) Kinsei 44 engine. This type was the Japanese navy's mainstay early in World War II. The D3A1, which was the world's first all-metal low-wing monoplane dive bomber, was the most numerous type used in the attack on Pearl Harbor on 7 December 1941.

The Japanese carrier task force launched 126 aircraft for the attack. The D3A was fitted with dive brakes similar to those of the German Junkers Ju 87. In the event, these had to be modified at an early development stage to eliminate excessive vibration. The improved D3A2, of which there were 1016 aircraft, entered service in the autumn of 1942. By this time the type was obsolescent and from 1943 most of the surviving aircraft were adapted as D3A2-K trainers. Many were later used for kamikaze attacks on Allied shipping.

This a D3A1 of the Yokosuka Kokota, shown in 1940 colours.

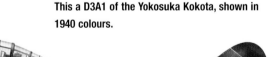

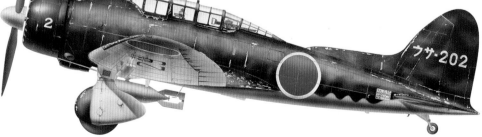

Dornier Do 217

The Dornier Do 217 was a larger, more powerful version of its predecessor, the Dornier Do 17. The prototype flew in August 1938 but it was not until August 1940 that the definitive aircraft materialized in the Do 217V-9.

COUNTRY OF ORIGIN: Germany

TYPE: (Do 217E-2) four-seat heavy bomber

POWERPLANT: two 1580hp (1178kW) BMW 801ML 14-cylinder radial engines

PERFORMANCE: maximum speed 515km/h (320mph); initial climb rate 216m (740ft) per minute; ceiling 9000m (29,530ft); range 2800km (1740 miles)

WEIGHTS: empty 10,535kg (23,225lb); maximum take-off 16,465kg (36,299lb)

DIMENSIONS: span 19m (62ft 4in); length 18.20m (59ft 8.5in); height 5.03m (16ft 6in)

ARMAMENT: one 15mm cannon in lower port side of nose, one 13mm machine gun in dorsal turret, one 13mm machine gun in ventral step position, 7.92mm forward-firing machine gun in nose, one 7.92mm machine gun in each cockpit side window; in the Do 217E-2/R19 subvariant, one remotely controlled 7.92mm rearward-firing machine gun in the tail cone, plus a bomb load of 4000kg (8818lb)

The Dornier Do 217 was much faster than its predecessor, the Do 17, and caused some problems for Britain's night defences.

The Do 217 was Dornier's response to a 1937 requirement for a long-range warplane optimzsed for the heavy level and dive-bombing roles, and it first flew in August 1938. The first operational model was the Do 217E of which some 800 aircraft were built in Do 217E-0 to Do 217E-4 subvariants with BMW 801 radial engines. These were followed by 950 examples of the Do 217K night bomber with a revised and unstepped nose, and finally the Do 217M development of the Do 217K with DB 603 inverted-Vee engines. Prototype and pre-production variants were the Do 217C bomber, Do 217P

high-altitude reconnaissance, and Do 217R missile-launching aircraft. There were also Do 217E and Do 217K subvariants armed with Hs 293 anti-ship missiles and Fritz-X guided bombs respectively. Do 217s sank the Italian ship *Roma* as she steamed to the Allies after Italy's surrender.

Baedecker raids

The Do 217 featured prominently in the so-called 'Baedecker' raids of 1942, when British cities of historic interest were targeted in reprisal for a Bomber Command attack on Lubeck. On 25 and 26 April Bath was attacked twice by the Do 217s of KG 2. The city suffered heavily, and in three more successive raids Norwich was attacked twice and York once, the latter city suffering heavy damage from incendiary bombs.

The Do 217N-2 night fighter differed from the bomber versions in that its dorsal gun turret was removed.

Farman F.221 and F.222

Designed to meet a requirement for a five-seat night bomber issued in 1929, the Farman 221 was the first four-engine night bomber to enter service with the Armee de l'Air.

The Farman heavy bomber was an ungainly machine, but performed surprisingly well in war conditions.

The F.220.01 bomber prototype was first flown in May 1932, and was then converted as a long-range mailplane. This was followed by the F.221.01 prototype that differed mainly in its redesigned vertical tail surface, fully enclosed nose and ventral gunner's positions, a semi-retractable 'dustbin' in place of the previous hatch position for the ventral gunner, and a considerably uprated powerplant.

Dropping leaflets and bombs

Next were 10 F.221BN.5 bombers with enhanced defensive armament, and then the F.222BN.5 that was produced in two variants as 11 F.222.1BN.5 machines with retractable main landing-gear units and 24 F.222.2BN.5 machines with a lengthened nose and

COUNTRY OF ORIGIN: France

TYPE: (F.222.2BN.5) five-seat heavy night bomber

POWERPLANT: four 970hp (723kW) Gnome-Rhône 14N-11/15 radial engines

PERFORMANCE: maximum speed 320km/h (199mph); climb to 4000m (13,125ft) in 13 minutes 30 seconds; service ceiling 8000m (26,245ft); range 2000km (1243 miles) with a 2500kg (5511lb) bomb load

WEIGHTS: empty 10,500kg (23,148lb); normal take-off 15,200kg (33,510lb); maximum take-off 18,700kg (41,226lb)

DIMENSIONS: span 36.00m (118ft 1.33in); length 21.45m (70ft 4.5in); height 5.19m (17ft 0.33in)

ARMAMENT: one 7.5mm trainable forward-firing machine gun in the nose turret, one 7.5mm trainable machine gun in the dorsal turret, and one 7.5mm trainable rearward-firing machine gun in the ventral 'dustbin' position, plus an internal bomb load of 4200kg (9259lb)

dihedralled outer wing panels. Twenty-four Farman 221/222s were in service with BG I/15 and II/15 at the outbreak of hostilities, initially carrying out leaflet-dropping from Reims in December 1939. In May and June 1940 they carried out several bombing missions, notably an attack on the BMW factory in Munich. Only one aircraft was lost during the entire campaign, and that was by accident. The end of the Battle of France found GB 15 at Istres. Most of the Farmans were destroyed in November 1942 during an Allied attack on Rabat.

Pictured here is an F.222.1 of the 2nd Escadrille, GB I/15, based at Reims-Courcy in May 1940.

Fokker T.VIII

A modern torpedo-bomber and reconnaissance floatplane, the Fokker T.VIII first flew in 1938. About 30 VIII-W production aircraft had been delivered, or were about to be delivered, at the time of the German invasion in 1940.

COUNTRY OF ORIGIN: Netherlands

TYPE: three-seat torpedo-bomber/reconnaissance floatplane

POWERPLANT: two 450hp (336kW) Wright Whirlwind R-975-E3 9-cylinder radial engines

PERFORMANCE: maximum speed 285km/h (177mph); service ceiling 6800m (22,310ft); range 2750km (1709 miles)

WEIGHTS: empty 3100kg (6834lb); maximum take-off 5000kg (11,023lb)

DIMENSIONS: span 18m (59ft); length 13m (42ft 8in); height 5m (16ft 5in); wing area 44 sq m (474 sq ft)

ARMAMENT: one fixed forward-firing .31in machine gun; one .31in machine gun on flexible mount in rear cockpit; plus up to 605kg (1334lb) of stores carried externally

This Fokker T.VIII is one of 25 examples requisitioned by the Luftwaffe.

Fokker's T-series floatplanes were specifically designed for service in the East Indies. The T.IV was one of Fokker's most ungainly designs, but was a tough, seaworthy combat aircraft and operated with distinction against the Japanese.

Wood and metal

The T.VIII-W was built in three versions: the T.VIII-Wg was of mixed wood-and-metal; the T-VIII-Wm was all metal; and the T-VIII-Wc was a scaled-up version in wood-and-metal with more powerful engines. Five were in service by June 1939, when the Fokker factory was

overrun. A total of 36 were built, 25 of which were requisitioned by the Luftwaffe (including five T.VIII-Wc aircraft on order for Finland). Eight survivors were flown to England on 14 May 1940, and were operated as No. 320 (Dutch) Squadron of RAF Coastal Command until they ran out of spares in late 1940. A landplane version, the T.VIII-L, was under construction in 1940 for Finland, but the sole example of this variant was taken over and completed by the Luftwaffe. The Fokker T.V, on which thre design of the T.VIII was based, equipped the Netherlands Air Arm's 1st Air Regiment at the time of the German invasion. The eight aircraft in service were soon expended in a series of gallant but suicidal bombing attacks, and were quickly reduced to a sole survivor.

The Fokker T.VIII was a tough and robust design, but only a few had been built when the Germans overran Holland in May 1940.

Lockheed Hudson

The Lockheed Hudson was developed at short notice in 1938 to meet a British requirement for a maritime reconnaissance aircraft to replace the Avro Anson in the squadrons of RAF Coastal Command.

COUNTRY OF ORIGIN: USA

TYPE: (Hudson Mk I) six-seat coastal reconnaissance bomber

POWERPLANT: two 1100hp (820kW) Wright GR-1820-G102A Cyclone nine-cylinder single-row radial engines

PERFORMANCE: maximum speed 357km/h (222mph); climb to 3050m (10,000ft) in 10 minutes; service ceiling 6400m (21,000ft); range 3154km (1960 miles)

WEIGHTS: empty 5484kg (12,091lb); maximum take-off 8845kg (19,500lb)

DIMENSIONS: span 19.96m (65ft 6in); length 13.50m (44ft 3.75in); height 3.32m (10ft 10.5in)

ARMAMENT: two 0.303in fixed forward-firing machine guns in upper part of forward fuselage, two 0.303in trainable machine guns in dorsal turret, two 0.303in machine guns in beam positions, and one 0.303in machine gun in ventral position; internal bomb load of 612kg (1350lb)

The Hudson was a development of the Model 14 Super Electra transport to meet a British and Commonwealth coastal reconnaissance bomber requirement, and first flew in December 1938. The first of 351 Hudson Mk I aircraft reached the UK in February 1939, and further deliveries of this type included the Hudson Mk II with the same Wright R-1820-G102A engines but different propellers, Hudson Mks III and IIIA, an improved version of the Mk I with 1200hp (895kW) GR-1820-G205A engines,

The Hudson Mk III of No 48 Squadron, illustrated here, was moved from the UK to Gibraltar in December 1942.

This Lockheed Hudson is in the service of the US Army Air Corps, where it bore the designation A-28.

Hudson Mks IV and IVA with 1050hp (918.5kW) Pratt & Whitney R-1830-SC3G Twin Wasp engines, Hudson Mk V with 1200hp (895kW) R-1830-S3C4G engines, and Hudson Mk VI delivered under Lend-Lease.

Notable actions

On 8 October 1939, an aircraft of No. 224 Squadron shot down a Dornier Do 18 reconnaissance seaplane off Jutland; this was the first German aircraft destroyed by an RAF aircraft operating from the British mainland in World War II. In the North Atlantic, one of the Hudson's most famous actions occurred on 27 August 1941, when the German submarine U-570 was attacked and damaged by an aircraft of No. 269 Squadron (Sqn Ldr J. Thompson) off Iceland. The Hudson circled the U-boat, which was unable to dive until its crew indicated that they wished to surrender. The Hudson was relieved by a Catalina and the submarine towed to Iceland by an armed trawler.

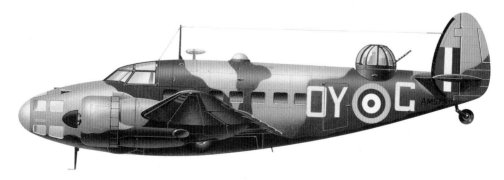

PZL P.37 Los

Similar to other Polish combat aircraft designed before World War II, the P.37 Los was slow to reach operational status, and came too late to have an impact on the invading Germans.

The P.37 Los proved an excellent combat type, but suffered from a lack of fighter protection in the Polish campaign.

COUNTRY OF ORIGIN: Poland

TYPE: (P.37B) four-seat medium reconnaissance bomber

POWERPLANT: two 918hp (684.5kW) PZL (Bristol) Pegasus XX nine-cylinder single-row radial engines

PERFORMANCE: maximum speed 445km/h (277mph); service ceiling 9250m (30,350ft); range 1500km (932 miles) with a 2200kg (4850lb) bomb load

WEIGHTS: empty 4280kg (9436lb); maximum take-off 8900kg (19,621lb)

DIMENSIONS: span 17.93m (58ft 10in); length 12.92m (42ft 4.7in); height 5.08m (16ft 8in)

ARMAMENT: one 7.7mm trainable forward-firing machine gun in nose position, one 7.7mm trainable rearward-firing machine gun in the dorsal position, and one 7.7mm trainable rearward-firing machine gun in ventral position, plus an internal bomb load of 2580kg (5688lb)

The Los ('Elk') was the most modern Polish warplane at the time of the German invasion, and technically compared favourably with the best medium bombers in the world. The P.37/I was the first of three prototypes and flew June 1936. Orders arrived for 180 production aircraft as the P.37A with 873hp (651kW) Pegasus XIIB engines, a single vertical tail surface and single-wheel main landing gear units, the P.37Abis with twin vertical surfaces, and the P.37B with an uprated powerplant, a redesigned cockpit, twin vertical surfaces and twin-wheel landing-gear units: deliveries amounted to 10, 20 and about 60 aircraft

This is a P.37B Los B of the Bomber Brigade, Dispositional Air Force, Polish Air Force, as it appeared in September 1939.

respectively. Export aircraft with Gnome-Rhône engines were ordered by Bulgaria, Romania, Turkey and Yugoslavia, but none was completed.

Triumph and disaster

In September 1939, Los attacks on invading German forces were very successful. On 4 September, the bombers struck the 1st and 4th Panzer Divisions, which lost 28 per cent of their strength as a result and were thrown into confusion. But the Polish Bomber Brigade was soon crippled by lack of fighter cover and suffered fearful losses.

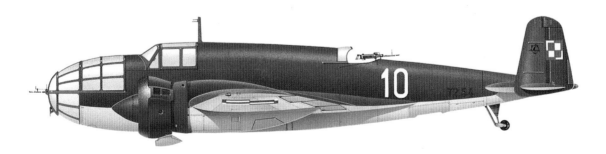

Short Stirling

The first of the RAF's trio of four-engined heavy bombers, the Short Stirling was designed to a 1936 specification and was first flown as a half-scale prototype in 1938. The full-scale prototype flew in May 1939.

COUNTRY OF ORIGIN: United Kingdom

TYPE: (Stirling Mk III) seven/eight-seat heavy bomber

POWERPLANT: four 1650hp (1230kW) Bristol Hercules XVI 14-cylinder two-row radial engines

PERFORMANCE: maximum speed 434km/h (270mph); initial climb rate 244m (800ft) per minute; service ceiling 5180m (17,000ft); range 3235km (2010 miles) with a 1588kg (3500lb) bomb load

WEIGHTS: empty 21,274kg (46,900lb); maximum take-off 31,752kg (70,000lb)

DIMENSIONS: span 30.2m (99ft 1in); length 26.59m (87ft 3in); height 6.93m (22ft 9in)

ARMAMENT: two 0.303in trainable forward-firing machine guns in the nose turret, two 0.303in trainable machine guns in the dorsal turret, and four 0.303in trainable rearward-firing machine guns in the tail turret, plus an internal bomb load of 6350kg (14,000lb)

The Short Stirling's operational ceiling suffered from the fact that the aircraft had too short a wing span.

The first four-engined heavy bomber to enter service with Bomber Command of the Royal Air Force during World War II, the Stirling was also the only British four-engined bomber to enter service after having been designed wholly as such. Even so, the Stirling was a workmanlike rather than inspired aeroplane largely as a result of the Air Ministry's demand for a span of less than 30.48m (100ft). The Stirling Mk I entered service in August 1940, and production of 2374 aircraft included 756 Mk I bombers with 1595hp (1189kW) Hercules XI

A Short Stirling III shown in the colours of of No. 7 Squadron, Pathfinder Force, 1943.

engines, 875 Mk III bombers with a revised dorsal turret, 579 Mk IV paratroop and glider-towing aircraft without nose and dorsal turrets, and 160 Mk V unarmed transports.

Transport and glider tug

Stirlings flew their last bombing mission in September 1944, having equipped 15 squadrons of RAF Bomber Command. By this time the aircraft had found its new role as a transport and glider tug. In this capacity the type suffered serious losses in September 1944, when the RAF's transport squadrons were making gallant but vain attempts to resupply the men of the 1st British Armoured Division, encirlced at Arnhem.

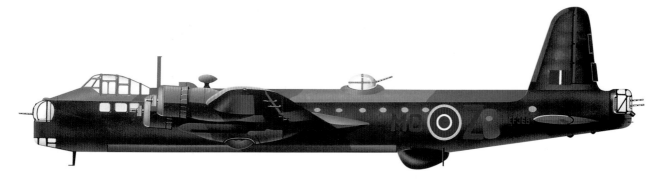

Avro Manchester

Designed to meet the requirments of Specification 13/36, which called for a twin-engined heavy bomber, the Manchester was powered by two 1760 Rolls-Royce Vulture engines which, in service, were to give constant trouble.

COUNTRY OF ORIGIN: United States

TYPE: (679 Mk I) seven seater medium bomber

PERFORMANCE: two 1760hp (1312kW) Rolls-Royce Vulture I X-type engines

POWERPLANT: maximum speed 426km/h (265mph); initial climb rate service ceiling 5850m (19,200ft); range 2623km (1630m) with 3674kg (8100lb) bombload

WEIGHT: empty 13350kg (29,432lb); maximum take-off 22680kg (50,000lb)

DIMENSIONS: span 27.46m (90ft 1in); length 20.98m (68ft 10in); height 5.94m (19 ft 6in)

ARMAMENT: eight 0.30in (7.7mm) trainable machine guns: two each in nose, dorsal turrets and four in tail, plus up to 4695kg (10,350lb) of bombs

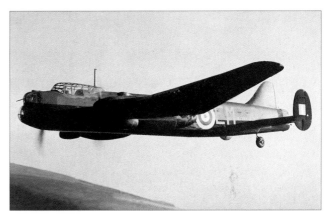

The Avro Manchester was a disaster operationally, but was the basis for the excellent Lancaster.

By the mid–1930s the steady improvement in aeronautical design allowed the Air Ministry to plan a new generation of advanced medium bombers, and in 1936 issued a requirement that elicited responses from both Avro and Handley Page. Both companies received prototype orders although the Handley Page did not progress beyond the drawing board. The Avro type was the Manchester medium bomber that first flew in July 1939 after an initial order for 200 aircraft had been built. The Manchester Mk I became operational in November 1940, and these 20

aircraft were followed by 180 examples of the Manchester Mk IA with larger endplate vertical surfaces on the tail, allowing the removal of the Mk I's centreline surface.

Let down by the engine
The Manchester flew its first operational mission in February 1941, when six aircraft of No. 207 Squadron attacked enemy warships in Brest harbour. On 12 March Manchesters attacked Germany for the first time with a raid on Hamburg. The Manchester had an ideal airframe, but unreliable Vulture engines, and retired in June 1942.

This is a Mk 1 of No 207 Squadron, RAF Bomber Command as it appeared in early 1941.

Mitsubishi G4M Betty

The G4M Betty was an excellent bomber, but in common with other Japanese combat aircraft it lacked sufficient protection, especially around its fuel tanks, which meant that it caught fire easily.

COUNTRY OF ORIGIN: Japan

TYPE: (G4M1 Model 11) seven-seat medium attack bomber

POWERPLANT: two 1530hp (1141kW) Mitsubishi MK4A Kasei 11 14-cylinder two-row radial engines

PERFORMANCE: maximum speed 428km/h (266mph); climb to 7000m (22,965ft) in 18 minutes; range 6033km (3749 miles)

WEIGHTS: empty 6800kg (14,991lb); maximum take-off 9500kg (20,944lb)

DIMENSIONS: span 25.00m (82ft 0.25in); length 20.00m (65ft 7.25in); height 6m (19ft 8.25in)

ARMAMENT: one 20mm trainable rearward-firing cannon in the tail position, one 7.7mm trainable rearward-firing machine gun in the dorsal blister position, and one 7.7mm trainable lateral-firing machine gun in each of the two beam positions, plus an external bomb and torpedo load of 800kg (1764lb)

A Japanese G4M crew undergo briefing before leaving on a mission.

The G4M was the ultimate expression of the Imperial Japanese Navy Air Force's desire to project land-based air power from its island garrisons deep into the Pacific Ocean for the destruction of enemy warships and the support of its own forces' amphibious operations. The G4M certainly possessed remarkable range but, as combat was to prove, this capability was purchased only at the expense of features that were just as important: crew protection, self-sealing fuel tanks and a sturdy structure able to absorb battle damage. Resulting from a 1937 requirement, the first of two G4M1 prototypes flew in October 1939, and the type entered service early in 1941. Production totalled 1200 G4M1 aircraft in variants such as

the Convoy Fighter escort (five 20mm trainable cannon), Model 11 attack bomber and Model 12 attack bomber, the last with MK4E engines.

Heavier armament, reduced agility

Following the G4M1, the G4M2 was built to the extent of 1154 aircraft for service from the middle of 1943 with an uprated powerplant, a laminar-flow wing, a larger tailplane, additional fuel capacity and heavier defensive armament for better overall capability but only at the cost of reduced agility. There were three attack bomber Model 22 subvariants (about 350 aircraft) with different armaments.

One of the final war roles played by the G4M1 of the 708th Kokutai, shown here, was as a carrier aircraft for the Ohka rocket-propelled suicide bomb.

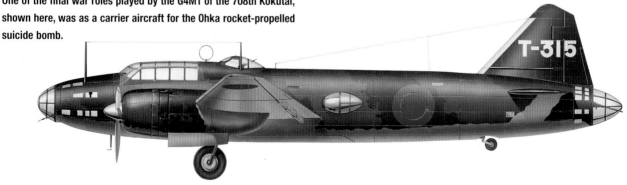

Ilyushin Il-2

In the autumn of 1938 the Soviet Air Force General Staff issued a requirement for a close support aircraft capable of destroying the latest tanks and armoured vehicles being mass-produced in Nazi Germany: the Ilyushin Il-2.

COUNTRY OF ORIGIN: USSR

TYPE: (Il-2M Tip 3) two-seat close support and anti-tank warplane

POWERPLANT: one 1770hp (1320kW) Mikulin AM-38F 12-cylinder Vee engine

PERFORMANCE: maximum speed 415km/h (258mph); climb to 5000m (16,405ft) in 15 minutes; service ceiling 6000m (19,685ft); range 800km (497 miles)

WEIGHTS: empty 4525kg (9976lb); maximum take-off 6360kg (14,021lb)

DIMENSIONS: span 14.60m (47ft 11in); length 12.00m (39ft 4.5in); height 3.40m (11ft 1.75in)

ARMAMENT: two 23mm fixed forward-firing cannon and two 7.62mm fixed forward-firing machine guns in the leading edges of the wings, and one 12.7mm trainable rearward-firing machine gun in the rear cockpit, plus an internal and external bomb and rocket load of 1000kg (2205lb)

The Il-2 was a close support aircraft capable of destroying the latest tanks and armoured vehicles being mass-produced in Nazi Germany.

Built in larger numbers (36,150 aircraft) and at a higher rate than any other warplane in history, the Il-2 was instrumental in the Soviet defeat of Germany by 1945. It entered service as the single-seat Il-2 three months before the German onslaught of June 1941 and was initially an indifferent warplane. The aircraft matured into a formidable ground-attack aircraft and was much feared by German forces on the ground. The Il-2 was followed by the Il-2M with the AM-38F engine and 23mm cannon, the Il-2M Tip 3 two-seat version of the Il-2M to allow the provision of rearward defence, and the Il-2M Tip 3M with

Shown here in hastily applied winter camouflage for the Stalingrad counter-offensive in February 1943 is an Il-2m3.

37mm rather than 23mm cannon for greater anti-tank capability. The Il-2 is probably best remembered for its part in the battle of Kursk.

A devastating destroyer

Following a series of experiments, Il-2s were fitted with two long-barrelled anti-tank cannon, and these were used with devastating effect at Kursk on the latest German Tiger and Panther tanks. During 20 minutes of concentrated attacks on the 9th Panzer Division, Il-2 pilots claimed to have destroyed 70 tanks. During the course of the battle, the 3rd Panzer Division, with a strength of 300 tanks and 180 men per infantry company, was claimed to have been reduced to 30 tanks and 40 men per infantry company, largely as a result of Il-2 attacks.

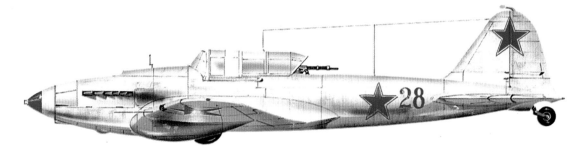

Heinkel He 177

The Heinkel He 177 Greif (Griffin) heavy bomber was plagued throughout its career by its engines. In an effort to reduce drag and enhance performance, its four Daimler-Benz engines were arranged in coupled pairs.

COUNTRY OF ORIGIN: Germany

TYPE: (He 177A-1/R1 Greif) five-crew heavy bomber

POWERPLANT: two 2700hp (2013kW) Daimler-Benz DB 606 (coupled DB 601) 24-cylinder engines

PERFORMANCE: maximum speed 510km/h (317mph); service ceiling 7000m (22,965ft); range 1200km (746 miles) with maximum bomb load

WEIGHTS: empty 18,040kg (39,771lb); maximum take-off 30,000kg (66,139lb)

DIMENSIONS: span 31.44m (103ft 1.75in); length 20.40m (66ft 11in); height 6.39m (20ft 11.75in)

ARMAMENT: one 7.92mm trainable forward-firing machine gun in nose position, one 20mm trainable forward-firing cannon in ventral gondola, two 7.92mm machine guns in ventral gondola, one 13mm machine gun in remotely controlled dorsal barbette, and one 13mm machine gun in tail position, plus a bomb load of 6000kg (13,228lb)

The Greif (Griffin) was a potentially excellent but ultimately disastrous warplane on which Germany expended enormous, largely wasted, resources. The type was schemed as a bomber able to deliver a large bomb load over a considerable range at high speed and altitude. To extract maximum performance from a four-engined powerplant by the minimization of drag, it was decided that the pair of engines on each wing should be coupled to drive a single propeller. This coupled powerplant was beset by enormous technical problems that were never wholly cured and resulted in numerous inflight fires. The first of eight He 177 prototypes flew in December 1939, and slow development meant that it was the summer of 1942 before they were ready.

Variants perform different functions
He 177A-3 early production aircraft entered service. The first He 177A-1 was delivered to I/KG 40 for operational trials. In all, 130 He 1877A-1s and 170 He 177A-3 production aircraft entered service. Subvariants of the latter were the He 177A-3/R3, which could carry three Hs 293 anti-ship missiles, the He 177A-3R/5, with a 75mm gun in a gondola under the nose, and the He 177A-3R/7 torpedo bomber. The last variant was the He 177A-5 (there was no A-4), which was structurally strengthened; 565 were delivered.

This He 177 is seen in Allied markings after the German surrender in May 1945. It was flown to Farnborough for flight testing by the RAF.

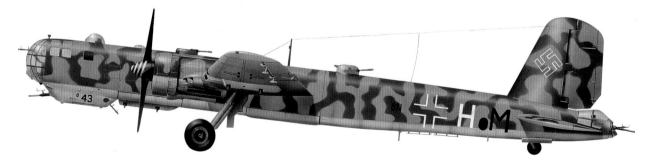

This is a Heinkel He 177A-3R1 of I/KG40, pictures at Chateaudun in late 1943.

Consolidated B-24 Liberator

The Consolidated B-24 Liberator made its operational debut in June 1942 with long-range raids from Egypt against the Romanian oilfields.

COUNTRY OF ORIGIN: USA

TYPE: (B-24D) ten-seat long-range heavy bomber

POWERPLANT: four 1200hp (895kW) Pratt & Whitney R-1830-43 or -65 14-cylinder two-row radial engines

PERFORMANCE: maximum speed 488km/h (303mph); climb to 6095m (20,000ft) in 22 minutes 0 seconds; service ceiling 9755m (32,000ft); range 4586km (2850 miles)

WEIGHTS: empty 14,490kg (32,605lb); maximum take-off 27,216kg (60,000lb)

DIMENSIONS: span 33.53m (110ft); length 20.22m (66ft 4in); height 4.46m (17ft 11in)

ARMAMENT: two 0.5in trainable forward-firing machine guns in the nose, two 0.5in trainable machines guns in each of the dorsal, ventral and tail turrets, and one 0.5in trainable lateral-firing machine gun in each of the waist positions, plus an internal bomb load of 3992kg (8800lb)

The B-24 Liberator provided the USAAF with a very long range strategic bomber especially suited for use in the Pacific.

Produced in a number of variants for a host of operational and training tasks, the Liberator was built in larger numbers (18,431 machines) than any other US warplane of World War II and was delivered in greater quantities than any other bomber in aviation history. First flown in December 1939, the single XB-24 prototype paved the way for seven YB-24 service test aircraft, and then nine B-24A initial production machines with heavier defensive armament. The XB-24 was then upgraded to the XB-24B standard that led to the nine B-24C bombers and then the first major production models, the B-24D (2738 aircraft), generally similar B-24E (791 aircraft) and B-24G (430

aircraft with a power-operated nose turret). The B-24 made its operational debut in June 1942 with the long-range raids from Egypt against Hitler's Romanian oilfields.

Paving the way

The B-24G paved the way for further Liberator development, including the B-24H (738 built by Consolidated, and 2362 made by Douglas and Ford), the B-24J that was an improved B-24H with an autopilot and other operational enhancements including a more capable bomb sight (6678 made by Consolidated, Douglas, Ford and North American), the B-24L with two manually operated tail guns rather than a turret (1667 aircraft from Consolidated and Ford), and the B-24M improved version of the B-24J (2593 aircraft from Consolidated and Ford). There were also LB-30, C-87 and RY transport, AT-22 trainer, F-7 long-range photo-reconnaissance and PB4Y-1 maritime reconnaissance variants.

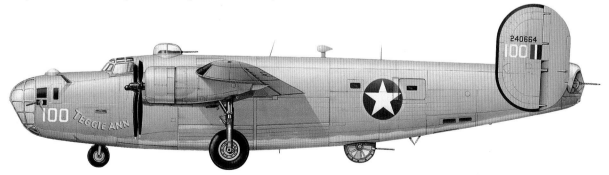

Pictured here is B-24D-85-CO Teggie Ann, the Group Lead Ship of the 47th Bomb Wing, 376th BG, painted in desert pink.

Douglas Boston Mk III

The Douglas Boston replaced the vulnerable Bristol Blenheim in the squadrons of No. 2 Group RAF from late 1941, and was itself eventually replaced by the far more effective de Havilland Mosquito.

COUNTRY OF ORIGIN: USA

TYPE: four-seat light attack bomber

POWERPLANT: two 1600hp (1193kW) Wright GR-2600-A5B Double Cyclone radial engines

PERFORMANCE: maximum speed 515km/h (320mph); initial climb rate 609m (2000ft) per minute; service ceiling 7470m (24,500ft); range 1996km (1240 miles) with reduced bomb load

WEIGHTS: empty 5534kg (12,200lb); normal take-off 8959kg (19,750lb); maximum take-off 9789kg (21,580lb)

DIMENSIONS: span 18.69m (61ft 4in); length 14.48m (47ft 6in); height 5.36m (17ft 7in)

ARMAMENT: four 0.303in fixed forward-firing machine guns on the sides of the forward fuselage, two 0.303in trainable machine guns in the dorsal position, and one 0.303in trainable machine gun in the ventral position, plus an internal bomb load of 907kg (2000lb)

The Douglas DB-7 Boston was essentially a stop-gap aircraft, but it gave good war service in all theatres.

The Douglas DB-7 attack bomber series began with the Model 7A. The first prototype, designated Model 7B, flew on 26 October 1939; 100 examples were ordered by France in February 1940 and 186, designated A-20 and A-20A, by the USAAC three months later. These, with the manufacturer's designation D RB-7, had a narrower and deeper fuselage than the original model. The French order was subsequently increased to 270 DB-7s and 100 DB-7As. France fell after 115 aircraft had been delivered; 95 of these survived in North Africa; the rest were diverted to

Britain. The DB-7 bombers taken over from French contracts were adapted as Havoc Mk I night-fighters. The type entered service in April 1941 with No. 85 Squadron.

Increased maximum take-off weight

The next light bomber was thus the Boston Mk III, a designation applied to a total of 753 aircraft including 452 DB-7Bs taken over from France. The Boston Mk III had improved self-sealing fuel tanks, added armour protection, a number of strengthening features to cater for an increased maximum take-off weight, a slightly longer fuselage, and increased fuel capacity. The aircraft were delivered to the UK from the summer of 1941, and entered service in October of the same year.

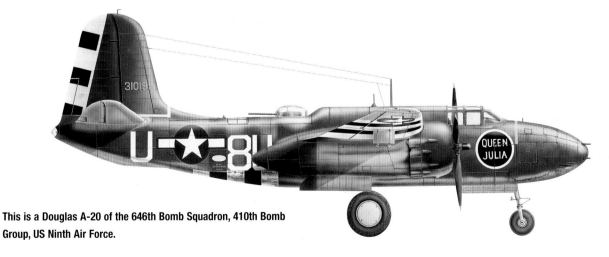

This is a Douglas A-20 of the 646th Bomb Squadron, 410th Bomb Group, US Ninth Air Force.

Handley Page Halifax

Although overshadowed by the somewhat more charismatic Lancaster, the Handley Page Halifax played a vital part in Bomber Command's night offensive against Germany, and performed many other roles besides.

Destined to become one of the most famous bomber aircraft of all time, the prototype HP.57 Halifax first flew on 25 October 1939.

COUNTRY OF ORIGIN: United Kingdom

TYPE: (Halifax Mk III) seven-seat heavy bomber

POWERPLANT: four 1615hp (1204kW) Bristol Hercules VI or XVI 14-cylinder two-row radial engines

PERFORMANCE: maximum speed 454km/h (282mph); climb to 6095m (20,000ft) in 37 minutes 30 seconds; service ceiling 7315m (24,000ft); range 3194km (1985 miles) with a 3175kg (7000lb) bomb load

WEIGHTS: empty 19,278kg (42,500lb); maximum take-off 29,484kg (65,000lb)

DIMENSIONS: span 30.07m (98ft 8in) or in later aircraft 31.59m (103ft 8in); length 21.74m (71ft 4in); height 6.12m (20ft 1in)

ARMAMENT: one 0.303in trainable forward-firing machine gun in the nose position, four 0.303in trainable machine guns in the dorsal turret, and four 0.303in trainable machine guns in the tail turret, plus an internal bomb load of 6577kg (14,500lb)

The Halifax was the main, but ultimately less glamorous partner to the Lancaster in the RAF heavy bomber force during the second half of World War II. It proved to be a highly versatile warplane, undertaking roles in maritime reconnaissance, transport and airborne forces. The two prototypes, of which the first flew in October 1939, were followed by the Halifax Mk I (84 aircraft in three series) that entered service in November 1940 with 1280hp (954kW) Rolls-Royce Merlin X Vee engines, and the Halifax Mk II (1977 aircraft in three sub-series) with 1390hp (1036kW) Merlin XX or XXII engines.

Seeing the war to the end

The Halifax Mk III saw a switch to Bristol Hercules radial engines; 2091 aircraft were made by five manufacturers. The Halifax Mk III remained in the front line to the end war's end. The Halifax Mk IV was a project only. The next operational variants were the Mks VI and VII, the former powered by the 1675hp Hercules 100 and the latter using the MK III's Hercules XVI. These were the ultimate bomber versions, and were produced in relatively small numbers. Some Halifax IIIs, Vs and VIIs were converted to paratroop dropping and glider towing. The Halifax MK VIII, which entered service just before the end of the war, was a transport version with faired-over gun positions and a detachable 3624kg (8000lb) freight pannier.

A Halifax Mk I of No 76 Squadron, which re-formed on a May 1941 from 'C' Flight of No 35 Squadron, the first Halifax unit.

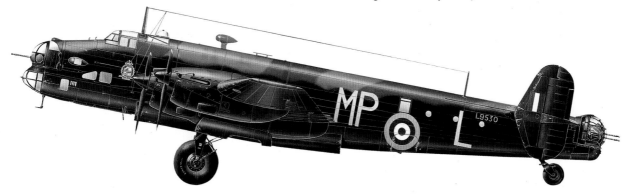

Petlyakov Pe-2

The Pe-2 was the outstanding Soviet tactical bomber of World War II, serving in large numbers. It played a decisive role in the air on the Eastern Front.

COUNTRY OF ORIGIN: USSR

TYPE: (Pe-2) three-seat multi-role attack bomber

POWERPLANT: two 1100hp (820kW) Klimov VK-105RA 12-cylinder Vee engines

PERFORMANCE: maximum speed 540km/h (335mph); climb to 5000m (16,405ft) in 7 minutes; service ceiling 8800m (28,870ft); range 1500km (932 miles) with a 2205lb (1000kg) bomb load

WEIGHTS: empty 5870kg (12,943lb); maximum take-off 8495kg (18,728lb)

DIMENSIONS: span 17.16m (56ft 3.7in); length 12.66m (41ft 6.5in); height 4.00m (13ft 1.5in)

ARMAMENT: two 7.62mm fixed forward-firing machine guns in the nose, one 7.62mm trainable rearward-firing machine gun in the dorsal position, and one 7.62mm trainable rearward-firing machine gun in the ventral position, plus an internal and external bomb load of 1600kg (3527lb)

It was not until late August 1941 that the Pe-2 was committed in any numbers, making low-level attacks on German armoured columns.

The Pe-2 may be regarded as the Soviet counterpart of the de Havilland Mosquito and Junkers Ju 88. It differed from its British and German counterparts in being optimized for the purely tactical role in a host of variants that were built to the extent of 11,427 aircraft. The origins of the design can be found in the VI-100 prototype for a high-altitude fighter that flew in 1939/40, but the design was then revised as the PB-100 dive-bomber with three rather than two crew members in unpressurized accommodation. The PB-100 prototype was a conversion of the second VI-100, and first flew in June 1940. Later in the same month the decision was taken for the PB-100 to be produced with a few minor changes as the Pe-2. It was not until late August 1941 that the Pe-2 was used in battle in any numbers, making low-level attacks on German armoured columns. Production of the Pe-2 rapidly got into its stride, 1405 aircraft being delivered to operational units in the second half of 1941. Pe-2 operations received a setback in the spring of 1942, when the Messerschmitt Bf 109F arrived on the Russian Front, and late in 1942 the Pe-2 FT appeared, this variant having two 1260hp Klimov M-105PF engines and a 12.7mm (0.50in) UBT machine gun in a dorsal turret.

Numerous variants

Numerous other Pe-2 variants were built during the aircraft's operational career. A multi-purpose fighter version armed with cannon, machine guns and underwing rockets, designated Pe-3, was also produced. Total production of the Pe-2/3, all variants, was 11,427 aircraft.

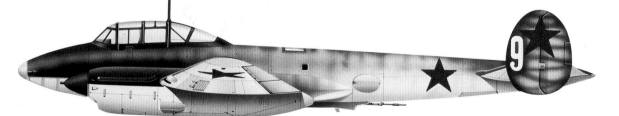

The Pe-2 had a neat, streamlined design, and made an enormous contribution to eventual Soviet victory.

Amiot 354

The Amiot 354 was a direct descendant of the Amiot 370, which captured several world speed records in 1938. It had an obvious military potential.

COUNTRY OF ORIGIN: France

TYPE: (Amiot 354B.4) four-seat medium bomber

POWERPLANT: two 1060hp (790kW) Gnome-Rhône 14N-48/49 14-cylinder two-row radial engines

PERFORMANCE: maximum speed 480km/h (298mph); climb to 4000m (13,125ft) in 8 minutes 42 seconds; service ceiling 10,000m (32,810ft); range 3500km (2175 miles) with an 800kg (1764lb) bomb load

WEIGHTS: empty 4725kg (10,417lb); maximum take-off 11,300kg (24,912lb)

DIMENSIONS: span 22.83m (74ft 10.75in); length 14.50m (47ft 6.75in); height 4.08m (13ft 4.5in)

ARMAMENT: one 20mm trainable rearward-firing cannon in the dorsal position, one 7.5mm trainable forward-firing machine gun in the nose, and one 7.5mm trainable rearward-firing machine gun in a ventral mounting, plus an internal bomb load of 1200kg (2646lb)

Developed in parallel with the Amiot 351, the Amiot 354 differed in that it featured a single- instead of a twin-fin tail unit.

Having produced the ungraceful Amiot 143 during the late 1920s, in the early 1930s the Amiot design team then created the beautiful Amiot 341 long-range mailplane. This aircraft paved the way for the Amiot 340 bomber prototype that developed by a number of steps into the Amiot 354B.4 production bomber. The 354B.4 was one of the best aircraft of its type to enter production before World War II. Some 900 of this type were ordered and offered good performance and potent defensive firepower. However, development and production delays meant that only about 45 had been completed before the fall of France in June 1940. The principal difference between the A-351 and A-354 variants of the design was that the former had twin fins; the tail units of both derivatives were interchangeable. The aircraft delivered went to equip GB 1, GB II/21 and GB I/34.

Night use only

The type was used operationally, but only at night. Total losses were 18, five on operations, the rest on the ground through air attack. The survivors were used mainly as high-speed transports, four being taken over by the Luftwaffe for clandestine operations. The aircraft pictured was the 39th delivered to the Armée de l'Air. After the war the sole surviving aircraft was operated by the French Air Ministry.

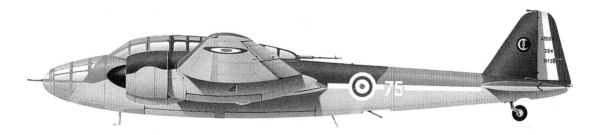

The most graceful of all France's piston-engined bombers, the Amiot 354 came too late to be of use in the Battle of France.

de Havilland Mosquito

The de Havilland DH.98 Mosquito saw service throughout the world as a day and night fighter, fighter-bomber, high-altitude bomber, pathfinder, anti-shipping strike aircraft, reconnaissance aircraft and trainer.

The Mosquito was a valuable photo-reconnaissance aircraft. This is a PR.Mk. XVI.

COUNTRY OF ORIGIN: United Kingdom

TYPE: (Mosquito B.Mk XVI) two-seat light bomber

POWERPLANT: two 1680hp (1253kW) Rolls-Royce Merlin 72/73 or 76/77 12-cylinder Vee engines

PERFORMANCE: maximum speed 668km/h (415mph); climb to 4570m (15,000ft) in 7 minutes 30 seconds; service ceiling 11,280m (37,000ft); range 2888km (1795 miles) with a 907kg (2000lb) bomb

WEIGHTS: empty 7031kg (15,500lb); maximum take-off 11,766kg (25,917lb)

DIMENSIONS: span 16.51m (54ft 2in); length 13.56m (44ft 6in); height 4.65m (15ft 3in)

ARMAMENT: an internal and external bomb load of up to 1814kg (4000 lb)

One of the most successful warplanes ever, and rivalled only by the Junkers Ju 88 for versatility, the Mosquito was developed as a private venture to provide the RAF with a bomber that possessed such outstanding performance that no defensive armament would be required. Built largely of a ply/balsa/ply sandwich material, the Mosquito Mk I prototype first flew in November 1940 and paved the way for a mass of variants. The bombers were the Mk IV (273 aircraft with a 2000lb/907kg bomb load), the Mk VII (25 Canadian-built aircraft), the Mk IX (54 aircraft with an uprated powerplant and, in some machines, the ability to carry a 4000lb/1814kg bomb load), the Mk XVI (1200 aircraft to a Mk IX standard upgraded with a pressurized cockpit), the Mk XX (145 Canadian-built aircraft with American equipment), and Mk 25 (400 Canadian-built aircraft). The first Mosquito B.IV bombers went to No. 105 Squadron at Marham, Norfolk, in May 1942, and made

their first operational sortie on the 31st. Five aircraft went to Cologne to photograph the damage caused by the previous night's 1000-bomber raid and to drop a few bombs. One Mosquito, hit by flak, crashed in the North Sea.

Low-level precision attacks

The Mosquito B.IV equipped twelve squadrons. The Mk VI fighter-bomber, which subsequently armed several squadrons of No. 2 Group, replaced such aircraft as the Lockheed Ventura. These squadrons carried out some daring low-level precision attacks during the last year of the war, including the raid on Amiens prison in February 1944 and attacks on Gestapo headquarters buildings in Norway and the Low Countries.

This is a Mosquito Mk.IV of No 105 Squadron, based at RAF Marham 1942-44.

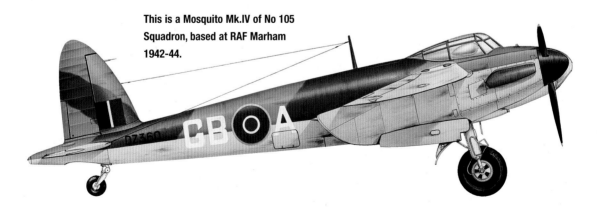

Martin B-26 Marauder

One of the most controversial Allied medium bombers of World War II, at least in the early stages of its career, the Glenn L. Martin 179 Marauder earned an unenviable reputation as a 'widow-maker' because of its handling characteristics.

COUNTRY OF ORIGIN: USA

TYPE: (Marauder Mk I) seven-seat medium attack bomber

POWERPLANT: two 1850hp (1379kW) Pratt & Whitney R-2800-5 18-cylinder two-row radial engines

PERFORMANCE: maximum speed 507km/h (315mph) at 4570 m (15,000ft); climb to 4570m (15,000ft) in 12 minutes 30 seconds; service ceiling 7620m (25,000ft); range 1609km (1000 miles)

WEIGHT: empty 9696kg (21,375lb); maximum take-off 14,515kg (32,000lb)

DIMENSIONS: span 18.81m (65ft); length 17.07m (56ft); height 6.05m (19ft 10in)

ARMAMENT: one 0.5in trainable forward-firing machine gun in the nose position, two 0.5in trainable machine guns in the dorsal turret, and one 0.5in trainable rearward-firing machine gun in the tail position, plus an internal and external bomb load of 4800lb (2177kg)

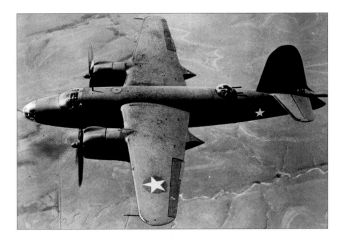

A war-weary B-26 Marauder pictured over mountainous terrain in New Guinea, where the type was greatly feared by the Japanese.

The B-26 Marauder was one of the most important tactical warplanes operated by the USA and its allies in World War II. The type was difficult for an inexperienced pilot to handle as a result of its high wing loading and high landing speed, but once mastered was an excellent warplane that achieved good results at a low loss rate.

Effective attacker

Entering service in 1941, the Marauder had a number of variants; the most important were the B-26 (201 machines), B-26A (139 machines with provision for a torpedo), B-26B and identical B-26C (1883 and 1235 machines with uprated engines), and B-26F and essentially similar B-26G (300 and 893 machines with increased wing

incidence). The British designations for the B-26A, B, C and F/G were Marauder Mk I, IA, II and III respectively. The first unit to re-arm with a mixture of B-26s and B-26As was the 22nd Bombardment Group at Langley Field in February 1941. Early in 1942 it moved to Australia, and became part of the US Fifth Air Force, attacking enemy shipping, airfields and installations in New Guinea and New Britain. Its first attack was a raid on Rabaul, on 5 April 1942. During the Battle of Midway, four B-26As of the 22nd and 38th BG attacked units of the Japanese fleet with torpedoes. The 22nd BG used B-26s exclusively until October 1943, when some B-25s were added.

This is a B-26G-1 of the 557th Bomb Squadron, 387th Bomb Group, based at Stony Cross, England, in July 1944.

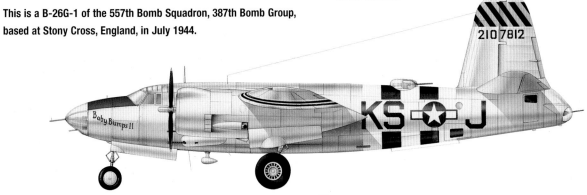

North American B-25

On 16 April 1942, the Mitchell leapt into the headlines when the aircraft carrier USS *Hornet*, from a position at sea 1075km (668 miles) from Tokyo, launched 16 B-25Bs for the first attack on the Japanese homeland.

COUNTRY OF ORIGIN: USA

TYPE: (B-25B) five-seat medium bomber

POWERPLANT: two 1700hp (1267kW) Wright R-2600-9 14-cylinder two-row radial engines

PERFORMANCE: maximum speed 483km/h (300mph); service ceiling of 7175m (23,500ft); range 2172km (1350 miles) with a 1361kg (3000lb) bomb load

WEIGHTS: empty 9072kg (20,000lb); maximum take-off 12,909kg (28,460lb)

DIMENSIONS: span 30.66m (67ft 7in); length 16.13m (52ft 11in); height 4.80m (15ft 9in)

ARMAMENT: one 0.3in trainable forward-firing machine gun in the nose position, two 0.5in trainable machine guns in the dorsal turret, and two 0.5in trainable machine guns in the ventral turret, plus an internal bomb load of 1361kg (3000lb)

One of the most important US tactical warplanes of World War II (9816 aircraft built), the Mitchell was a medium bomber that was also a potent anti-ship warplane. The origins of the type can be found in 1938, when North American gambled that the US Army Air Corps would need a new attack bomber.

Classic tactical warplane

Work commenced on the NA-40 that first flew in January 1939 before conversion into the NA-40B. The concept was then refined as the NA-62, subsequently ordered as 24 B-25 initial production aircraft, delivered from February 1941. Later deliveries comprised 40 and 120 B-25A and

One of the most important US tactical warplanes of World War II, the North American B-25 Mitchell flew for the first time in January 1939.

B-25B aircraft, the former with self-sealing fuel tanks and the latter with dorsal and ventral turrets but no tail gun position. The B-25B was followed into service by the virtually identical B-25C, 1619 of which were built at North American's Inglewood plant, and B-25D, with uprated engines, an autopilot, external hardpoints for one 907kg (2000lb) torpedo or eight 113kg (250lb) bombs, provision for forward-firing machine guns in packs attached to the sides of the forward fuselage. The two variants were used in most theatres of war, and 533 B-25C/D aircraft were delivered to the RAF as Mitchell Mk IIs to supplement an earlier delivery of 23 Mitchell Mk I (B-25B) aircraft. Eight squadrons of the RAF's No. 2 Group used the Mitchell. The dedicated anti-shipping version of the Mitchell was the B-25G.

USAAF Mitchells operated effectively against Japanese forces in New Guinea, carrying out low-level strafing attacks in the wake of Allied bombing operations.

Avro Lancaster

During World War II, the Avro Lancaster became synonymous with RAF Bomber Command's ongoing night offensive against Nazi Germany. Its most famous exploit was the breaching of the Ruhr Dams in May 1943.

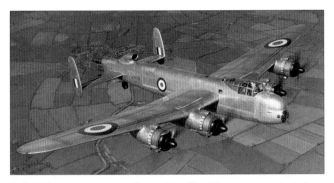

In the later war years some Lancasters, like this one, were adapted as test beds for early jet engines, seen here installed in the tail.

The most successful and celebrated heavy night bomber used by the RAF in World War II, the Lancaster was a development of the Manchester with the revised powerplant of four Rolls-Royce Merlin Vee engines. The Lancaster first flew on 9 January 1941, and entered service from the beginning of 1942.

A sturdy aircraft

The original Lancaster Mk I soon developed an enviable reputation as a sturdy aircraft that handled well in the air, possessed moderately good performance and had good defensive and offensive firepower. The fact that the type was essentially 'right' from its beginning is indicated that few changes were made other than minor engine and

equipment details in the course of a long production run that saw the delivery of 7378 aircraft. It grew clear that the Rolls-Royce Merlin engine would not be able to keep pace with the manufacture of the airframes designed to use it, so the US licence-built version, the Packard V-1650, was used in its Merlin 28, 38 or 224 forms instead. When this engine was installed in the Lancaster Mk I, the aeroplane was known as the Lancaster Mk III (later B.Mk III and finally B.Mk 3), and deliveries of this model totalled 3020 aircraft. The Lancaster Mk III was also selected for production in Canada by Victory Aircraft Ltd. of Toronto, which delivered 430 examples of the Lancaster Mk X (later B.Mk X and finally B.Mk 10).

COUNTRY OF ORIGIN: United Kingdom

TYPE: (Lancaster Mk I) seven-seat heavy night bomber

POWERPLANT: four 1640hp (1223kW) Rolls-Royce Merlin XX, 22 or 24 12-cylinder Vee engines

PERFORMANCE: maximum speed 462km/h (287mph); initial climb rate 76m (250ft) per minute; service ceiling 5790m (19,000ft); range 2784km (1730 miles) with a 5443kg (12,000lb) bomb load

WEIGHTS: empty 16,783kg (37,000lb); maximum take-off 29,484kg (65,000lb)

DIMENSIONS: span 31.09m (102ft); length 21.18m (69ft 6in); height 6.25m (20ft 6in)

ARMAMENT: two 0.303in trainable machine guns in the nose turret, two 0.303in trainable machine guns in the dorsal turret, four 0.303in trainable machine guns in the tail turret, and provision for one 0.303in trainable machine gun in a ventral turret, plus an internal bomb load of 8165kg (18,000lb)

This is a Lancaster Mk I of No. 467 Squadron, RAAF, an Australian unit operating with No. 5 Group Bomber Command.

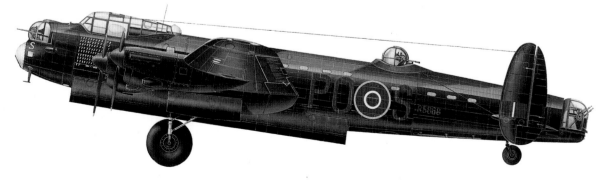

Tupolev Tu-2

Soviet pilots were particularly enthusiastic about the Tu-2, their reports stressing its substantial bomb load, excellent combat radius, good defensive armament and its ability to fly on one engine.

COUNTRY OF ORIGIN: USSR

TYPE: (Tu-2S) four-seat medium attack bomber

POWERPLANT: two 1850hp (1379kW) Shvetsov ASh-82FN 14-cylinder two-row radial engines

PERFORMANCE: maximum speed 547km/h (340mph); climb to 5000m (16,405ft) in 9 minutes 30 seconds; service ceiling 9500m (31,170ft); range 2100km (1305 miles)

WEIGHTS: empty 7474kg (16,477lb); maximum take-off 11,360kg (25,044lb)

DIMENSIONS: span 18.86m (61ft 10.5in); length 13.80m (45ft 3.3in); height 4.56m (14ft 11in)

ARMAMENT: two 20mm fixed forward-firing cannon in wing roots, one 12.7mm trainable rearward-firing machine gun in rear of the cockpit, one 12.7mm machine gun in dorsal position, and one 12.7mm machine gun in ventral position, plus an internal bomb load of 4000kg (8818lb)

The prototype first flew on 29 January 1941 and subsequent flight testing showed that the aircraft's outstanding performance.

First flown in ANT-58 prototype form during January 1941, the Tu-2 was one of the best high-speed bombers to see service in World War II, but was built in larger numbers (2500 or more aircraft) after the end of the war than during the conflict. Developed via the ANT-59 and ANT-60 prototypes then the Tu-2 pre-production model, the Tu-2S initial production model was delivered from the spring of 1944 as a Tu-2 development with uprated engines and heavier armament. It proved to possess excellent operational capabilities in the attack-bomber and ground-attack roles.

Effective against fortified towns

The only two other models to see significant combat service during World War II were the Tu-2D long-range model and the Tu-2R photo-reconnaissance model. The Tu-2 first saw action on a large scale in June 1944 on the Karelian (Finnish) front. In its primary bombing role, the Tu-2 carried out some extremely effective missions in the closing months of the war, particularly against fortified enemy towns. The aircraft was also used extensively in the brief Soviet campaign against the Japanese Kwantung Army in Manchuria in August 1945. Chinese Tu-2s were encountered by UN fighter pilots during the Korean War, proving easy targets for jet fighters such as the F-86 Sabre.

This aircraft is a Tu-2S of a Soviet bomber regiment as it appeared when it was operating on the Eastern Front in 1945.

Grumman TBF Avenger

Destined to be the most successful torpedo-bomber of World War II, the Grumman Avenger was a pre-war design, two XTBF-1 prototypes being ordered in April 1940. The first of these flew on 1 August 1941.

Making a disastrous combat debut in the Battle of Midway (June 1942), the TBF matured as the classic torpedo bomber of World War II. The first of two XTBF-1 prototypes made their maiden flight in August 1941. Grumman then built only the TBF-1 model (2289 aircraft completed by March 1945) with subvariants such as the baseline TBF-1, winterized TBF-1J Avenger, TBF-1P photo-reconnaissance type, TBF-1B (402 aircraft) delivered to the UK, TBF-1C (764 aircraft) with two 0.5in machine guns, TBF-1CP photo-reconnaissance type, TBF-1D for the anti-submarine role with radar and

Grumman Avengers of the Fleet Air Arm, Mediterranean Theatre, 1944.

COUNTRY OF ORIGIN: USA

TYPE: (TBF-1C) three-seat carrierborne and land-based torpedo bomber

POWERPLANT: one 1700hp (1268kW) Wright R 2600 8 Cyclone 14 14-cylinder two-row radial engine

PERFORMANCE: maximum speed 414km/h (257mph); climb to 3050m (10,000ft) in 13 minutes; service ceiling 6525m (21,400ft); range 4321km(2685 miles)

WEIGHTS: empty 4788kg (10,555lb); maximum take-off 7876kg (17,364lb)

DIMENSIONS: span 16.51m (54ft 2in); length 12.42m (40ft 9in); height 4.19m (13ft 9in)

ARMAMENT: two 0.5in fixed forward-firing machine guns in the leading edges of the wing, one 0.5in Browning trainable rearward-firing machine gun in the dorsal turret, and one 0.3in rearward-firing machine gun in ventral position, plus torpedo, bomb and rocket load of 1134kg (2500lb)

This Grumman Avenger of the Fleet Air Arm is wearing the 'invasion stripes' adopted for the D-Day landings, June 1944.

underwing rockets, TBF-1E with podded air-to-surface radar, and TBF-1L with a retractable searchlight.

Multiple uses

The Royal Navy's wartime Avengers were mostly TBF-1Bs. In Fleet Air Arm service they were designated Tarpon Mk I and then Avenger Mk I. Production was moved to the Eastern Division of General Motors, which built 2882 aircraft as the TBM-1 and -1C; 334 of these went to the Royal Navy as the Avenger II. Eastern then completed 4664 TBM-3s, with uprated Cyclone engines and wings strengthened to support rocket projectiles or a radar pod; 222 were delivered to the Royal Navy as the Avenger III. The Avenger was not retired from US Navy service until 1954. The TBM-3 Avenger also served with the French Aeronavale, and was used during the Suez landings of 1956.

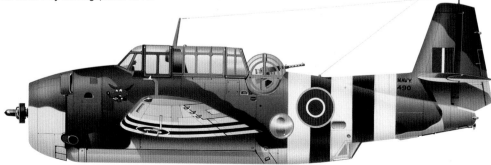

Curtiss SB2C Helldiver

The Curtiss SB2C Helldiver was slow to reach operational status and its problems were never completely cured, but it played an important part in the destruction of the Japanese Navy.

COUNTRY OF ORIGIN: USA

TYPE: (SB2C-1C) two-seat carrierborne and land-based scout and dive-bomber

POWERPLANT: one 1700hp (1268kW) Wright R-2600-8 Cyclone 14 14-cylinder two-row radial engine

PERFORMANCE: maximum speed 452km/h (281mph); climb to 3050m (10,000ft) in 7 minutes 42 seconds; ceiling 7375m (24,200ft); range 2213 km (1375 miles)

WEIGHTS: empty 4588kg (10,114lb); maximum take-off 7626kg (16,812lb)

DIMENSIONS: span 15.15m (49ft 8.26in); length 11.18m (36ft 8in); height 4.00m (13ft 1.5in)

ARMAMENT: two 20mm fixed forward-firing cannon in the leading edges of the wing, and two 0.3in trainable rearward-firing machine guns in the rear of the cockpit, plus an internal and external torpedo, bomb and depth-charge load of 1361kg (3000lb)

The Curtiss Helldiver played an enormous part in the destruction of the remaining surface units of the Japanese fleet.

The SB2C Helldiver, schemed as successor to the SBD Dauntless, first flew in XSB2C-1 prototype form in December 1940. The aircraft was never fully effective but it was built to the extent of 7200 aircraft including the A-25 land-based version for the US Army as well as the Canadian-built SBF and SBW (300 and 894 respectively) by Canadian Fairchild and Canadian Car & Foundry. The type made its operational debut in November 1943. The main models were the SB2C-1 baseline variant (978 aircraft in two subvariants), SB2C-3 (1112 aircraft) with the 1900hp (1417kW) R-2600-20 engine, SB4C-4 (2045 aircraft in two subvariants) with provision for additional underwing stores, and SB2C-5 (970 aircraft) with increased fuel tankage. The type entered service with the US Navy in December 1942, but it did not make its operational debut until 11 November 1943, in an attack on the island of Rabaul. In this attack, three heavy and two light carriers organized in two carrier task forces struck hard at Japanese shipping, sinking one destroyer and damaging other vessels, including two cruisers.

Invaluable in the Pacific theatre

The USAAF took delivery of 900 examples of a ground-attack version, the A-25A. The Helldiver was such great value in the Pacific theatre that the US Navy absorbed almost the entire production of over 7000 aircraft.

Seen here is a Helldiver in use with a US Navy training squadron, its role denoted by the orange band around the fuselage.

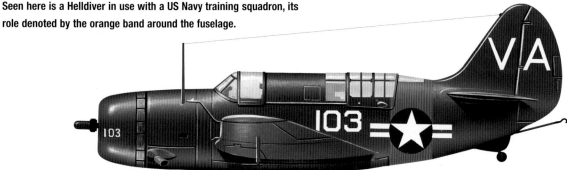

Messerschmitt Me 410 Hornisse

Developed from the unsuccessful Me 210, the Me 410 Hornisse (Hornet) was used both as a bomber-destroyer and a fast attack aircraft, making hit-and-run night raids on Britain.

COUNTRY OF ORIGIN: Germany

TYPE: (Me 410A-1/U2) two-seat heavy fighter

POWERPLANT: two 1750hp (1305kW) Daimler-Benz DB 603A 12-cylinder inverted-Vee engines

PERFORMANCE: maximum speed 624km/h (388mph); climb to 6700m (21,980ft) in 10 minutes 42 seconds; service ceiling 10,000m (32,810ft); range 1670km (1050 miles)

WEIGHTS: empty 7518kg (16,574lb); normal take-off 9651kg (21,276lb)

DIMENSIONS: span 16.35m (53ft 7.75in); length 12.48m (40ft 11.5in); height 4.28m (14ft 0.5in)

ARMAMENT: two 20mm fixed forward-firing cannon in the nose, two 20mm fixed forward-firing cannon in a ventral tray, two 7.92mm fixed forward-firing machine guns in the nose, and one 13mm machine gun in each of the two barbettes on the sides of the fuselage

The Me 410 Hornisse was a better proposition than its predecessor, the Me 210, and was a good high-speed bomber.

This multi-role warplane served as successor to the unsuccessful Messerschmitt Me 210 heavy fighter and was a more capable, successful warplane. The failings of the Me 210 had been solved just before the type's cancellation, and it was from this ultimately excellent type that the Me 410 was evolved with basically the same revised aerodynamic and structural features in combination with modified outer wing panels and the different powerplant of two Daimler-Benz DB 603A inverted-Vee piston engines. The Me 410 first flew in prototype form during autumn 1942, and there were 1137 production aircraft in variants such as the Me 410A (three major variants) and the Me 410B. Five major variants of the 410B were produced with the DB 603G engines. The B-5 anti-shipping torpedo bomber, the B-7 day

reconnaissance and B-8 night reconnaissance aircraft were still in experimental stage at the war's end.

Destroying intruders

In night attacks on Britain, the enemy fighter-bombers penetrated UK air space at up to 30,000 feet before diving on their objectives and making a high-speed exit. These tactics caused problems for the RAF's night fighters, since following an enemy aircraft in a dive meant that radar contact was often lost because of ground returns. The answer was to extend the night-fighter patrol lines well out to sea, and many intruders were trapped and destroyed in this way.

This is a Messerschmitt Me 410 of ZG76, which used the type against American daylight bomber formations.

Boeing B-29 Superfortress

The B-29 Superfortress was famous as the bomber that brought strategic air warfare to the Japanese home islands during the last year of the war, and then carried out the nuclear attacks on Hiroshima and Nagasaki.

COUNTRY OF ORIGIN: USA

TYPE: (B-29) nine-seat long-range heavy bomber

POWERPLANT: four 2200hp (1640kW) Wright R-3350-23 18-cylinder two-row radial engines

PERFORMANCE: maximum speed 576km/h (358mph); climb to 6095m (20,000ft) in 38 minutes; service ceiling 9710m (31,850ft); range 9382km

WEIGHTS: empty 31,816kg (70,140lb); normal take-off 47,628kg (105,000lb); maximum take-off 56,246kg (124,000lb)

DIMENSIONS: span 43.05m (141ft 2.75in); length 30.18m (99ft); height 9.02m (29ft 7in)

ARMAMENT: one 20mm trainable rearward-firing cannon and two 0.5in trainable rearward-firing machine guns in the tail position, and two 0.5in trainable machine guns in each of two dorsal and two ventral barbettes, plus an internal bomb load of 9072kg (20,000lb)

The B-29 Superfortress brought the strategic bombing war to the Japanese home islands.

In 1951 the Royal Air Force acquired 87 B-29s, one of which is seen here. The type was known as the Washington in RAF service.

The B-29 is generally remembered as the warplane which, on 6 and 9 August 1945, dropped atomic weapons destroying Hiroshima and Nagasaki, causing Japan to surrender. Yet by this time the B-29 had been at the forefront of a campaign to neutralize the war-making potential of Japan by burning her cities, destroying her communications network and crippling her industries.

Turbocharged engines

First entering service in the summer of 1944, the Superfortress was an extremely clean bomber with turbocharged engines. The baseline B-29 (2458 built) was complemented by the B-29A, 1119 of which had greater span and a four- rather than two-gun forward dorsal barbette, and the B-29B (310 built) delivered with reduced defensive armament but a greater bomb load and higher speed. The B-29s that dropped the atomic bombs, 'Enola Gay' and 'Bock's Car,' belonged to the 509th Bombardment Wing (Provisional), which was to become the principal US nuclear weapons trials unit. The B-29 continued to be the mainstay of the USAF Strategic Air Command for several years after 1945, and saw almost continual action during the three years of the Korean War. Production of the B-29 ended in May 1946, after 3970 aircraft had been built, but the basic design subsequently underwent several modifications. These included the SB-29 (search and rescue), TB-29 (trainer), WB-29 (weather reconnaissance) and KB-29 (tanker).

Aichi B7A Ryusei 'Grace'

By the time the B7A Rysei – code-named Grace by the Allies – became operational the Japanese carrier fleet had been destroyed, and the 114 aircraft built were forced to operate from land bases.

The B7A Rysei (Shooting Star) was developed in response to a 1941 Japanese Navy requirement for a new torpedo bomber.

In 1941 the Imperial Japanese navy air force requested a carrierborne attack bomber to replace the Nakajima B6N torpedo bomber and Yokosuka D4Y dive-bomber. Aichi's response was the AM-23 design, and the first of nine B7A1 prototypes flew in May 1942. The development programme was delayed by engine problems, and it was April 1944 before the type entered production as the B7A2, which offered very good handling and excellent performance. Although production in three factories was planned, only two came on stream and production totalled a mere 105 aircraft (80 from Aichi and 25 from the 21st

The principal variant, the B7A-2, did not enter service until 1944, production having been delayed by an earthquake.

Naval Air Arsenal). These had to operate from land bases as the Japanese navy now had no operational aircraft carriers.

Kamikaze suicide attackers

The B7A was one of several types brought into service by the Imperial Japanese Navy in the closing months of the Pacific war, but Japanese production couldn't cope with demand and in any case the Japanese carrier force had been decimated. Some B7As were expended in kamikaze suicide attacks, and others were held back to launch strikes against a US invasion fleet that never came. The Imperial Japanese Navy ceased all hostilities on 21 August, 1945.

COUNTRY OF ORIGIN: Japan

TYPE: (B7A2) two-seat carrierborne and land-based torpedo bomber and dive-bomber

POWERPLANT: one 2000hp (1491kW) Nakajima NK9C Homare 12 18-cylinder two-row radial engine

PERFORMANCE: maximum speed 566.5km/h (352mph); climb to 4000m (13,125ft) in 6 minutes 55 seconds; service ceiling 11,250m (36,910ft); range 3038km (1888 miles)

WEIGHTS: empty 3810kg (8400lb); maximum take-off 6500kg (14,330lb)

DIMENSIONS: span 14.40m (47ft 3in); length 11.49m (37ft 8.33in); height 4.07m (13ft 4.5in)

ARMAMENT: two 20mm fixed forward-firing cannon in wing, and one 13mm trainable rearward-firing machine gun in the rear cockpit, plus an internal bomb and torpedo load of 800kg (1764lb)

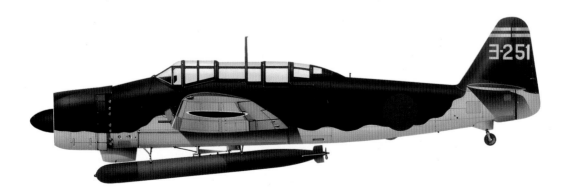

Douglas A-26 Invader

First flown in July 1942, the A-26 Invader was ordered in three variants: the A-26 three-seat attack bomber, the A-26A two-seat night fighter and intruder, and the A-26B three-seat heavy assault aircraft.

COUNTRY OF ORIGIN: USA

TYPE: (A-26B) three-seat light attack and reconnaissance bomber

POWERPLANT: two 2000hp (1491kW) Pratt & Whitney R-2800-27 or -71 18-cylinder two-row radial engines

PERFORMANCE: maximum speed 571km/h (355mph); climb to 3050m (10,000ft) in 7 minutes 0 seconds; service ceiling 6735m (22,100ft); range 2092km (1300 miles) with a 1361kg (3000lb) bomb load

WEIGHTS: empty 10,147kg (22,370lb); maximum take-off 12,893kg (42,300lb)

DIMENSIONS: span 21.34m (70ft); length 15.42m (50ft 7in); height 5.64m (18ft 6in)

ARMAMENT: six 0.5in fixed forward-firing machine guns, two 0.5in trainable machine guns in dorsal barbette, two 0.5in trainable rearward-firing machine guns in optional ventral barbette, and provision for eight 0.5in fixed forward-firing machine guns in four underwing packs, plus a bomb load of 2722kg (6000lb).

The Douglas A-26 Invader first flew in July 1942 and was ordered for the USAAF in three variants.

Produced in small numbers by World War II standards, the A-26 flew in more conflicts than any other warplane. The type was ordered in XA-26, XA-26A and XA-26B prototype forms, the first as a three-seat attack bomber with a potential 2268kg (5000lb) bomb load, the second as a two-seat night-fighter and intruder with radar and cannon, and the third as a three-seat heavy attack fighter with a 75mm cannon. The type first flew in July 1942. The A-26B (1355 built) entered service in Europe during November 1944, and at the same time became operational in the Pacific. Powered by two 1491kw (2000hp) Pratt &

Whitney radial engines giving a top speed of 571km/h (377mph) the A-26B was the fastest US bomber of the war.

Low-level precision attacks

The A-26B and A-26C both saw extensive service as night intruders during the Korean War. Some were supplied to France and were used in Indo-China post-war, while 70 were converted to B-26K standard for counter-insurgency operations during the early part of the Vietnam War. During the early days of the Korean War successful night attacks on enemy convoys depended on visual contact and accurate target information, as the A-26s carried no short-range navigation radar or blind bombing equipment. In Vietnam, the A-26s operated against convoys using the Ho Chi Minh Trail.

This A-26 Invader wears the code letters of the 552nd Squadron, 386th Bomb Group, US Ninth Army Air Force.

Arado Ar 234 Blitz

The Ar 234 Blitz (Lightning) was the world's first operational jet bomber. The origins of the type can be traced to a 1940 requirement issued by the German Air Ministry for a fast, turbojet-powered reconnaissance aircraft.

Early-model Ar 234s were designed to take off from a trolley and land on a skid, as seen here.

COUNTRY OF ORIGIN: Germany	

TYPE: (Ar 232 V3) single-seat reconnaissance aeroplane

POWERPLANT: two 1852lb (8.24kN) Junkers Jumo 109-004A-0 turbojet engines

PERFORMANCE: (estimated) maximum speed 780km/h (485mph); service ceiling 16,370m (36,090ft); range 2000km (1243 miles)

WEIGHTS: empty 4800kg (10,580lb); maximum take-off 8000kg (17,637lb)

DIMENSIONS: span 14.40m (47ft 3.25in); length 12.65m (41ft 5.5in)

ARMAMENT: none

The Blitz was the only turbojet-powered bomber to achieve operational status in World War II, and as such was an important milestone in the development of military aviation. The origins of the type can be traced to a 1940 requirement issued by the German air ministry for a turbojet-powered fast reconnaissance aeroplane. This resulted in the development of no fewer than 18 prototypes with a powerplant of two Junkers 004 or four BMW 003 turbojets, provision for rocket-assisted take-off units, a cabin with or without pressurization and a pilot's ejection seat, and a clumsy combination of a drop-away trolley for take-off and extendable skids for landing. Four B-1s were operated by Sonderkommando Götz based at Rheine from July 1944 for the reconnaissance role, and

from early October reconnaissance missions were being flown over Allied-occupied Europe and the British Isles.

Ludendorff bridge attacks

The bomber version of the Ar 234 equipped KG 76 from October 1944, flying its first missions during the Ardennes offensive in December. They were very active in the early weeks of 1945, one of their most notable missions being the ten-day series of attacks on the Ludendorff bridge at Remagen, captured by the Americans in March 1945. Few Ar 234 sorties were flown after March, but an experimental Ar 234 night fighter unit, the Kommando Bonow, with two Ar 234s converted to carry upward-firing cannon, operated until the end of the war.

This is an Arado Ar 234 of KG 76, which began operations during the Ardennes offensive of 1944.

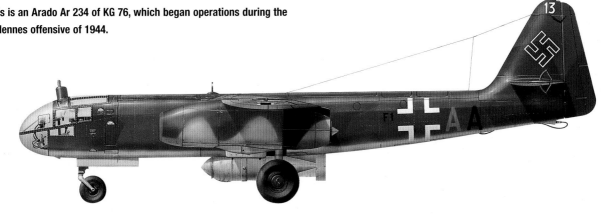

Boeing B-47 Stratojet

The B-47 was a radical departure from conventional design, featured a thin, flexible wing – based on wartime research data – with 35 degrees of sweep and carrying six turbojets in underwing pods.

COUNTRY OF ORIGIN: USA

TYPE: (B-29) nine-seat long-range heavy bomber

POWERPLANT: four 2200hp (1640kW) Wright R-3350-23 18-cylinder two-row radial engines

PERFORMANCE: maximum speed 576km/h (358mph); climb to 6095m (20,000ft) in 38 minutes; service ceiling 9710m (31,850ft); range 9382km (5830 miles)

WEIGHTS: empty 31,816kg (70,140lb); normal take-off 47,628kg (105,000lb); maximum take-off 56,246kg (124,000lb)

DIMENSIONS: span 43.05m (141ft 2.75in); length 30.18m (99ft); height 9.02m (29ft 7in)

ARMAMENT: one 20mm trainable rearward-firing cannon and two 0.5in trainable rearward-firing machine guns in the tail position, and two 0.5in trainable machine guns in each of two dorsal and two ventral barbettes, plus an internal bomb load of 9072kg (20,000lb)

This B-47 is seen taking off with the aid of its rocket-assisted take-off gear (RATOG).

Boeing began studies of jet bombers in 1943, but the discovery of German research in swept wings spurred the Model 450. The design had evolved from the straight winged Model 424, through the swept wing Model 448 with fuselage mounted turbojets, until the final design was dubiously bought by the USAAF in October 1945. The bomber was at the peak of its career in the mid-1950s when it was probably the most important military aircraft in the West. The first production model was the B-47B was powered by J47-GE23 engines and featured a number of structural modifications, including a strengthened wing. It carried underwing fuel tanks, and was fitted with eighteen JATO solid fuel rockets to give an emergency take-off

thrust of up to 9060kg (20,000lb). The most numerous version of the Stratojet was the B-47E, which first flew on 30 January 1953; 1359 of this type were built.

Electronic intelligence gathering

Variants included the RB-47E reconnaissance aircraft, the QB-47E radio-controlled drone and the ETB-47 crew trainer, as well as the RB-47H and RB-47K, which were modified for electronic intelligence gathering. Peak strength in SAC was reached in 1957, when about 1800 of all models were in service. Thirty-two were RB-47H models, built for electronic reconnaissance missions, with room for equipment and three Electronic Warfare officers.

Seen here is an RB-47H of the 55th Strategic Reconnaissance Wing USAF, whose aircraft made overflights of Soviet territory during the Cold War.

Ilyushin Il-28 'Beagle'

Designed as a tactical light bomber to replace the piston-engined Tupolev Tu-2, Ilyushin's Il-28 was the mainstay of the Soviet Bloc's tactical striking forces during the 1950s.

COUNTRY OF ORIGIN: USSR

TYPE: three seat bomber and ground attack/dual control trainer/torpedo carrier

POWERPLANT: two 2700kg (5952kg) Klimov VK-1 turbojets

PERFORMANCE: maximum speed 902 km/h (560mph); service ceiling 12,300m (40,355ft); range 2180km (1355 miles); with bomb load 1100km (684 miles)

WEIGHTS: empty 12890kg (28,418lb); maximum take-off 21,200kg (46,738lb)

DIMENSIONS: span 21.45sq m (231 sq ft); length 17.65m (57ft 10.75in); height 6.70m (21ft 11.8in); wing area 60.80sq m (654.47sq ft)

ARMAMENT: two 23mm NR-23 fixed cannon in nose, two 23mm NR-23 trainable cannon in tail turret; internal bomb capacity of up to 1000kg (2205lb), maximum bomb capacity 3000kg (6614lb); torpedo version had provision for two 400mm light torpedoes

The Ilyushin Il-28 Beagle provided the Soviet tactical air forces with an excellent ground-attack aircraft.

First appearing in prototype form as early as 1948, the Il-28 gave Eastern Bloc armed forces the same degree of flexibility and duration of service the Canberra did for Britain. The prototype was powered by two Soviet-built turbojets developed directly from the Rolls-Royce Nene, supplied by the British government in a fit of contrition. The unswept wing is set high, well back on the fuselage to reduce the movement caused by fuel tanks located in the rear fuselage and the aft gunner's compartment. The gunner also acts as the radio operator, with the navigator housed in the glazed nose section. After a public fly-past during the 1950 May Day parade, Soviet units began to equip with the Il-28 in some numbers. The aircraft served with all Warsaw Pact light bomber units between 1955–70. A trainer version (Il-28U) was also produced.

Exports to Soviet-friendly countries

Five hundred Il-28s were supplied to China, where the type was also built under licence as the Harbin H-5. Egypt acquired 60, of which 20 were destroyed at Luxor by French F-84F Thunderstreaks during the Suez crisis of 1956. Il-28s formed part of the package of combat aircraft and missiles delivered to Cuba in 1962, provoking the so-called 'missile crisis' and a swift US response. A small number, possibly ten aircraft, were supplied to the North Vietnamese Air Force in the 1960s. The USAF deployed Convair F-102 interceptors to the theatre to counter this potential threat, which in fact never materialized.

Seen here is an Il-28 of the Chinese People's Air Force, which used the type in considerable numbers.

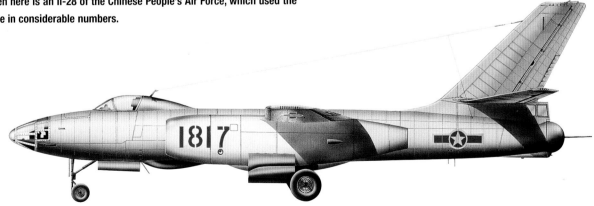

BAe (English Electric) Canberra

Originally designed for the radar bombing role, the English Electric Canberra was the greatest success story of Britain's post-war aviation industry. The first prototype Canberra B.1 flew on 13 May 1949.

The Canberra T.4 was used to train Canberra crews. It was used by No. 231 Operational Conversion Unit, Bassingbourn.

COUNTRY OF ORIGIN: United Kingdom

TYPE: two-seat interdictor aircraft

POWERPLANT: two 2948kg (6500lb) Rolls-Royce Avon Mk 101 turbojets

PERFORMANCE: maximum speed at 12,192m (40,000ft) 917km/h (570mph); service ceiling 14,630m (48,000ft); range 4274km (2656 miles)

WEIGHTS: empty not published; approximately 11,790kg (26,000lb); maximum take-off 24,925kg (54,950lb)

DIMENSIONS: span 29.49m (63ft 11in); length 19.96m (65ft 6in); height 4.78m (15ft 8in); wing area 97.08sq m (1045sq ft)

ARMAMENT: internal bomb bay with provision for up to 2727kg (6000lb) of bombs, plus an additional 909kg (2000lb) of underwing pylons

Before he left Westland aircraft, the company established by his family in 1915, W.E.W. Petter already had a scheme for a jet bomber. To meet specification B.3/45 he eventually planned an unswept aircraft with a broad wing for good behaviour at high altitude. The A.1 bomber was to be fast enough to escape interception whilst carrying a 2727kg (6000lb) bomb load over a radius of 750 nautical miles. It was to have a radar sight for blind attacks in all conditions. The prototype, which flew for the first time on 13 May 1949 at the hands of Roland 'Bee' Beamont, amazed everybody with its low-level manoeuvrability. Delays in the development of the bombsight resulted in an initial order for a tactical day bomber, designated B.Mk 2.

The Canberra was a huge export success. This example is in the markings of the Air Force of Zimbabwe.

Reconnaissance variants

The first of these entered service with No. 101 Squadron on 25 May 1951. A photo-reconnaissance version, the PR.3, was issued to No. 540 Squadron in 1953; the PR.7 and PR.9 were two subsequent reconnaissance variants. The next variant was the T.4 dual control trainer, which appeared in 1954; this was followed by the B.5, a converted PR.3 intended for target marking, but only a few examples were built before it was superseded by the B.6, a more powerful version with Rolls-Royce Avon 109 engines. The B(I)6 was an interim night interdictor version, superseded by the B(I)8; the latter featured some radical modifications, the most notable being an entirely redesigned fuselage nose and offset fighter-type cockpit. The Canberra was built under licence in the USA as the Martin B.57, and in Australia as the B.20 and T.21.

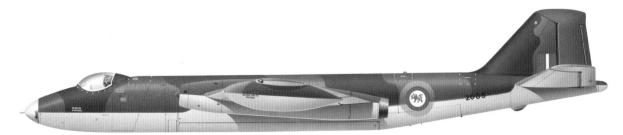

Vickers Valiant

Designed to meet the requirements of Specification B.9/48, the Vickers Valiant was the first of the RAF's trio of 'V-Bombers', and played a vital part in building up Britain's strategic nuclear deterrent.

COUNTRY OF ORIGIN: United Kingdom

TYPE: strategic bomber

POWERPLANT: four 4559kg (10,050lb) Rolls-Royce Avon 204 turbojets

PERFORMANCE: maximum speed at high altitude 912km/h (567mph); service ceiling 16,460m (54,000ft); maximum range 7242km (4,500 miles)

WEIGHTS: empty 34,4191kg (75,881lb); maximum loaded with drop tanks 79,378kg (175,000lb)

DIMENSIONS: span 34.85m (114ft 4in); length 33m (108ft 3in); height 9.8m (32ft 2in); wing area 219.43sq m (2,362sq ft)

ARMAMENT: internal weapons bay with provision for up to 9525kg (21,000lb) of conventional or nuclear weapons

Apart from its sleek design and electrical systems, the Valiant was completely conventional.

Designed to the same B.35/46 specification as the Avro Vulcan and Handley Page Victor, the prototype Vickers 660 did not fully meet the detailed requirements of that document. The fact that it could be rapidly put into production and represented a lower risk than the radical Vulcan or Victor encouraged the government to order it under the reduced specification B.9/48. The prototype 660 first flew in May 1951; the first pre-production aircraft flew in December 1953, and service deliveries began in August the next year. Most aircraft were finished in white anti-flash paint and had an extended tail cone housing

avionics. They were active during the Suez campaign, and conducted all-live trials with British air-dropped nuclear weapons, but were assigned to low-level missions in 1963.

Low-level, high-speed penetration

The whole fleet was scrapped a year later. The Valiant tended to be overshadowed by the RAF's later V-bombers, the Vulcan and Victor, but the contribution it made to the development of Bomber Command's nuclear alert force was immeasurably important. Not only did it pioneer the introduction of free-fall nuclear weapons into operational service; it also acted as trials aircraft for the Avro Blue Steel stand-off bomb, the weapon that would have given the V-bombers a chance of survival in the 1960s. It pioneered the techniques that would have ensured the V-force's viability in the event of a war alert. The Valiant B.Mk.2 was a one-off prototype stressed for low-level, high-speed penetration.

A Valiant B.1 is seen here in the grey-green camouflage scheme adopted after the type was assigned to NATO in the tactical bombing role.

Avro Vulcan

The first bomber in the world to employ the delta-wing platform, the Avro Type 698 Vulcan prototype (VX770) flew for the first time on 30 August 1952. The first production Vulcan B.Mk.1 was delivered in July 1956.

COUNTRY OF ORIGIN: United Kingdom

TYPE: long-range strategic bomber

POWERPLANT: four 7711kg (17,000lb) Rolls-Royce Olympus 201 turbojets

PERFORMANCE: maximum speed at altitude 1038km/h (645mph); service ceiling 19,810m (65,000ft); range with normal bomb load 7403km (4600 miles)

WEIGHTS: maximum take-off 113,398kg (250,000lb)

DIMENSIONS: span 33.83m (111 ft); length 30.45m (99ft 11in); height 8.28m (27 ft 2in); wing area 368.26sq m (3964sq ft)

ARMAMENT: internal bay with provision for up to 9526kg (21,000lb) of bombs

A Vulcan flying at low level over the sea makes a striking image. Some Vulcans were used for maritime radar reconnaissance.

In the early 1950s, the Royal Air Force issued Specification B.14/46, which called for an aircraft that could deliver nuclear weapons from any of its bases in the world. The Avro Vulcan was thus designed ostensibly as a high level nuclear bomber. The first production aircraft were designated B. Mk 1 and entered service in this role in 1956 with the V-bomber force. The B.Mk 1 was joined in service in 1960 by the improved Vulcan B.Mk 2.

Flight refuelling

These aircraft were furnished with flight refuelling equipment. It was also intended that this variant would carry the Blue Steel or American Skybolt stand-off nuclear weapons, but, with the adoption of Polaris, these plans never materialized. Existing Vulcan squadrons converted to the B.Mk 2A in 1962-64. In 1969 the RAF's Vulcan force was assigned to NATO and CENTO in the free-fall bombing role. In May 1982, Vulcans carried out attacks on the Falkland Islands in support of British operations to recapture these from Argentina. Total Vulcan production was 136 aircraft, including the two prototypes and 89 B.2s. The last operational Vulcans were six aircraft of No. 50 Squadron, converted to the flight refuelling role.

This Vulcan B.2 XM600 eventually crashed near RAF Coningsby, Lincolnshire, on 17 January 1977 as the result of a fire in the bomb bay and wing. The crew escaped.

Boeing B-52 Stratofortress

The B-52 was the mainstay of the West's airborne nuclear deterrent forces for three decades, but it was in a conventional role that it went to war – Vietnam, the Gulf War, the former Yugoslavia, Afghanistan and Iraq.

The B-52 has been in continuous service with Strategic Air Command in one form or another since 1955, with service life for the current generation of B-52H aircraft to end in 2038. Development of this remarkable warhorse began in 1945. The first prototype flew on 2 October 1951, and deliveries of 98 A, B and C models began in June 1955. Boeing extensively revised the forward control system for the tail-mounted armament of four 0.5in machine guns for the B-52D (Model 464-201-7). The company built 101 B-52Ds at its Seattle plant, before production was moved to Wichita where another 69 were completed. Deliveries of this version began in 1956. The aircraft had been designed to carry stand-off nuclear weapons but in 1964 a rebuilding programme began to

This aerial photograph gives a realistic impression of the B-52's massive wing span.

allow it to carry 105 'iron bombs'. Following the B-52E (100 built) and the B-52F (89) came the major production variant, the B-52G. The B-52G was the first aircraft to be armed with a long-range stand-off air-to-surface missile, the North American GAM-77 Hound Dog.

Hound Dogs

In 1962 there were 592 Hound Dogs on SAC's books, and it stayed in operational service until 1976. B-52G production totalled 193 examples, 173 of these converted in the 1980s to carry 12 Boeing AGM-86B Air Launched Cruise Missiles. The last version was the B-52H, intended to carry the cancelled Skybolt air-launched IRBM, but was modified to carry four Hound Dogs instead.

COUNTRY OF ORIGIN: USA

TYPE: long-range strategic bomber

POWERPLANT: eight 4536kg (10,000lb) Pratt & Whitney J57 turbojets

PERFORMANCE: maximum speed at 7315m (24,000ft) 1014km/h (630mph): service ceiling 13,720–16,765m (45,000–55,000ft); standard range with maximum load 9978km (6,200 miles)

WEIGHTS: empty 77,200–87,100kg (171,000–193,000lb); loaded 204,120kg (450,000lb)

DIMENSIONS: span 56.4m (185ft); length 48m (157ft 7in); height 14.75m (48ft 3in); wing area 371.60sq m (4,000sq ft)

ARMAMENT: remotely controlled tail mounting with four 0.5in machine guns; normal internal bomb capacity 12,247kg (27,000lb) including all SAC special weapons; modified to take up to 31,750kg (70,000lb) of conventional bombs on internal and external pylons

The last version was the B-52H which can carry up to 20 air-launched cruise missiles.

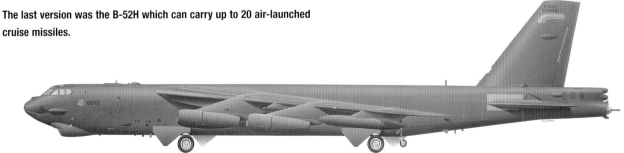

Sud-Ouest SO.4050 Vautour

Designed from the outset to carry out three tasks – all-weather interception, close support and high-altitude bombing – the Sud-Ouest SO4050 Vautour (Vulture) flew for the first time on 16 October 1952.

COUNTRY OF ORIGIN: France

TYPE: two-seat medium bomber

POWERPLANT: two 3503kg (7716lb) SNECMA Atar 101E-3 turbojets

PERFORMANCE: maximum speed 1105km/h (687mph); service ceiling more than 15,000m (49,210ft)

WEIGHTS: empty 10,000kg (22,046lb); maximum take-off 20,000kg (44,092lb)

DIMENSIONS: span 15.09m (49ft 6in); length 15.57m (51ft 1in); height 4.5m (14ft 9in)

ARMAMENT: internal bomb bay with provision for up to 10 bombs, and underwing pylons for two bombs up to 450kg (992lb), or two drop tanks

The Sud-Ouest Vauthour was used by the French Air Force in both the light-bomber and night-fighter roles.

This is a Vautour IIA of the Israeli Air Force. The type saw action in the Six Day War of 1967.

After World War II, the French aircraft industry strived to make up for five lost years, particularly in the new science of jet propulsion. By mid-March 1951 Sud-Ouest had flown the prototype of an advanced high-performance twin-jet bomber, designated the S.O. 4000. From this was developed the S.O. 4050. The S.O. 4050 differed quite considerably from its predecessor, with swept-wing surfaces and the engines mounted in nacelles beneath the wing. One of the three S.O. 4050 prototypes was completed as a two-seat bomber, with Armstrong Siddeley Sapphire turbojets and a glazed bomb-aiming position in the nose. The aircraft was designated S.O. 4050-3, and first flew on 5 December 1954. Evaluation of the aircraft led to production orders for 40, powered by the SNECMA Atar turbojet that was common to all variants.

Entering service

The first of 70 Vautour IINs entered service in 1956 with the 6e Escadre de Chasse, followed by EC 30 in the following year, while the first of 40 Vautour IIBs entered service in December 1957 with 1/92 'Bourgogne' and 2/92 'Aquitaine' at Bordeaux. The final version of the Vautour was the IIBR, a bomber-reconnaissance variant. The close-support version of the Vautour, the IIA, was not used by the French Air Force, but 20 examples were supplied to Israel, together with four IINs, and saw action in the Six Day War of 1967.

Handley Page Victor

The last in a long line of Handley Page bombers, and the last of the RAF's trio of V-bombers, the HP.80 Victor's design owed much to research into the crescent wing carried out by the German Arado and Blohm & Voss firms.

COUNTRY OF ORIGIN: United Kingdom	
TYPE: four-seat air-refuelling tanker	
POWERPLANT: four 9344kg (20,600lb) Rolls-Royce Conway Mk 201 turbofans	
PERFORMANCE: maximum speed at 12,190m (40,000ft) 1030km/h (640mph); maximum cruising height 18,290m (60,000ft); range with internal fuel 7,400km (4,600 miles)	
WEIGHTS: empty 41,277kg (91,000lb); maximum take-off 105,687kg (233,000lb)	
DIMENSIONS: span 36.58m (120ft); length 35.05m (114ft 11in); height 9.2m (30ft 1.5in); wing area 223.52sq m (2,406sq ft)	

A Victor K.2 about to touch down at Goose Bay, Labrador, during an overseas deployment.

The Victor was the third and last of the V-bombers to go into service with RAF Bomber Command in 1955–58. The design of the aircraft, with the crescent-shaped wing for maximum cruising speed was a superb technical achievement. Development time was long and when the Victor had finally entered service it could be intercepted by fighters or shot down by missiles. The number ordered was correspondingly small and the cost was high.

Converted and improved

Survivors of the 50 B.Mk 1 and B.Mk 1H Victors built were converted by Handley Page to K.Mk 1 two-point

and K.Mk 1H three-point tanker standard between 1965 and 1967. Thirty-four improved Victor B.Mk 2s, with increased power and redesigned airframe were supplied to the RAF. The B.Mk.2 was designed to carry the cancelled US Skybolt IRBM, and two squadrons (Nos 100 and 139) were armed with the Avro Blue Steel stand-off missile. The Victor B.(PR).Mk.1 and B.(PR).Mk.2 were photo-reconnaissance variants, both serving with No. 543 Squadron. In 1964-65 the earlier Victors were converted to the flight refuelling tanker role as B.(K).Mk 1s and 1As, and 27 Mk.2s were converted to K.Mk.2 tankers in 1973–74. These aircraft participated in the Gulf War.

Two Victor B.2 squadrons, Nos 100 and 139, were armed with the Avro Blue Steel stand-off missile, seen here recessed under the fuselage.

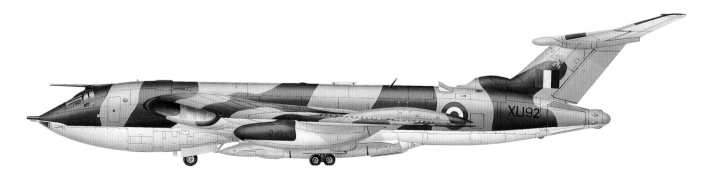

Douglas A3 Skywarrior

First flown on 28 October 1952, the Douglas A3D (later A-3) Skywarrior was the first carrier-borne bomber designed for strategic nuclear strike, and was intended to operate from the US Navy's Forrestal-class carriers.

COUNTRY OF ORIGIN: USA

TYPE: carrier-based strategic bomber

POWERPLANT: two 5635kg (12,400lb) Pratt & Whitney turbojets

PERFORMANCE: maximum speed 982km/h (610mph); service ceiling 13,110m (43,000ft); range with maximum fuel 3220km (2000 miles)

WEIGHTS: empty 17,875kg (39,409lb); maximum take-off 37,195kg (82,000lb)

DIMENSIONS: span 22.1m (72ft 6in); length 23.3m (76ft 4in); height 7.16m (23ft 6in); wing area 75.43sq m (812sq ft)

ARMAMENT: two remotely controlled 20mm cannon in tail turret, plus provision for 5443kg (12,000lb) of conventional or nuclear weapons in internal bomb bay

The A3D Skywarrior gave the US navy a substantial carrier-borne nuclear strike capability.

The A3 Skywarrior was designed by a team led by Ed Heinemann at El Segundo. It was the first carrier-based strategic nuclear bomber, built to be operated from the deck of the Forrestal class of carriers that came into service in 1948. Both the outer wings and tail folded hydraulically to minimize the space it occupied on deck. An advanced blind-bombing radar was carried in the nose.

Service in Vietnam

The first of the two prototypes flew on October 28, 1952 powered by two Westinghouse engines, but the failure of this programme meant that the Pratt & Whitney J57-P-6 powered that production A3D-1. Deliveries began in March 1956 to the US Navy's VH-1 attack squadron. Later variants saw much service in Vietnam as electronic intelligence and electronic countermeasures platforms. In 1953, Douglas received an order from the USAF to modify the A3D as a land-based reconnaissance and bomber aircraft. The first production version, the B-66B (72 built), began to replace the Martin B-57 Canberra in the USAF's tactical bomber wings from March 1956. It was preceded slightly by the RB-66B reconnaissance aircraft, of which 145 examples were built; this being followed by the RB-66C and the WB-66D (77 built of both sub-types), the latter a specialized weather reconnaissance version. The RB-66C equipped two tactical reconnaissance wings. Many B-66/RB-66 aircraft were modified for the electronic warfare role as EB-66s and saw action in the Vietnam War, its equipment being used to detect emissions from the tracking radar of the SA-2 Guideline surface-to-air missile and employing countermeasures against it.

The A3 Skywarrior was nicknamed 'The Whale' by the Navy crews who flew and maintained it.

Tupolev Tu-16 'Badger'

Deployed in the mid-1950s, Tupolev's Tu-16 was the most effective of Russia's trio of new strategic bombers, the others being the Myasishchev Mya-4 Bison and Tupolev Tu-95 Bear.

The Tu-16 gave the Soviet Air Force and Navy a formidable nuclear strike capability.

COUNTRY OF ORIGIN: USSR

TYPE: medium bomber

POWERPLANT: two 9500kg (20.944lb) Mikulin RD-3M turbojets

PERFORMANCE: maximum speed at 6000m (19,685ft) 960km/h (597mph); service ceiling 15,000m (49,200ft); combat range with maximum weapon load 4800km (2983 miles)

WEIGHTS: empty 40,300kg (88,846lb); maximum take-off 75,800kg (167,110lb)

DIMENSIONS: span 32.99m (108ft 3in); length 34.80m (114ft 2in); height 10.36m (34ft 2in); wing area 164.65sq m (1772.3sq ft)

ARMAMENT: one forward and one rear ventral barbette each with two 23mm NR-23 cannon; two 23mm NR-23 cannon in radar-controlled tail position; internal bomb bay for up to 9000kg (19,842lb) of free-fall bombs

The 'Badger-A' was the first operational version of the Tu-16 medium bomber, designated Tu-88 in prototype form. The Tu-88 was first flown in the winter of 1952, and full-scale production commenced in 1953. The principal sub-variant of the Badger-A was the Tu-16A, configured to carry the USSR's air-deliverable nuclear weapons. This variant featured prominently in the Soviet atmospheric nuclear test programme of the mid-1950s. Other sub-variants were the Tu-16T torpedo bomber, Tu-16K

airborne lifeboat carrier, Tu-16N wingtip-to-wingtip flight refuelling tanker and an undesignated probe-and-drogue tanker, some converted as Tu-16G (Tu-104G) for training Aeroflot crews and for fast mail services.

Anti-shipping and maritime reconnassaince

The next major variant, the Tu-16KS-1 Badger-B, was similar to Badger-A but initially carried the KS 1 Komet III (AS 1 Kennel) anti-shipping missile. The Tu-16K-10 Badger-C was an anti-shipping version armed with the K-10 (AS-2 Kipper) ASM under the fuselage, with a Puff Ball radar in a broad flat nose radome. Tu-16K-26 Badger-C Mod was a conversion of the Tu-16K-10. The Tu-16R Badger-D was a conversion of the Badger C for maritime reconnaissance, featuring Elint and mid-course missile guidance systems, an enlarged chin radome, and new radomes projecting from bomb bay. The Badger-F was also a maritime reconnaissance version. The Badger-E was basically a Badger-A with a battery of cameras in the bomb bay for high altitude maritime reconnaissance. The Badger-G was armed with two AS-5 Kelt or AS-6 Kingfish ASMs and was a dedicated anti-shipping version, while the Badger-J was equipped for barrage jamming in the A- to I-bands. The Badger-L was one of the last variants in a long line of electronic intelligence gatherers.

This Soviet Naval Air Arm Badger-C is armed with the As-6 Kingfish air-to-surface anti-ship missile.

Tupolev Tu-95/Tu-142

Given the NATO reporting name Bear, the Tupolev Tu-95 flew for the first time on 12 November 1952. The type entered service with the Soviet Strategic Air Forces (Dalnaya Aviatsiya) in 1957.

COUNTRY OF ORIGIN: USSR

TYPE: strategic bomber/maritime warfare aircraft

POWERPLANT: four 11,186kW (15,000hp) Kuznetsov NK-12MV turboprop engines

PERFORMANCE: maximum speed 805km/h (500mph); service ceiling 13,400m (44,000ft); range 12,550km (7800 miles)

WEIGHTS: 154,000kg (340,000lb) loaded

DIMENSIONS: span 48.50m (159ft); length 47.50 (155ft 10in); height 11.78m (38ft 8in)

ARMAMENT: six 23mm (0.91in) cannon; weapons load of up to 11,340kg (25,000lb)

Although designed as a strategic nuclear bomber, the Tu-95 found its true vocation as a maritime surveillance aircraft.

The initial Tu-95M Bear-A freefall nuclear bomber was followed by the Tu-95K-20 Bear-B of 1961, this being a maritime attack and reconnaissance version with a large radome under the nose and a Kh-20 (AS-3 Kangaroo) cruise missile. The Tu-95KD was similar, but was fitted with an flight refuelling probe. The Tu-95KM Bear-C, thought to be a new-build variant, was a specialized maritime reconnaissance version, as was the similar Bear-D, while the Bear-E and -F were upgraded variants with a new electronics suite. These and later aircraft were designated Tu-142. Later models include the Bear-H, equipped to carry up to four cruise missiles, and the Bear-J, a very long frequency (VLF) communications platform based on the Bear-F. Eight Tu-142s were supplied to the Indian Navy.

Nonstop long transit flights

In terms of longevity the Bear has matched Boeing's venerable B-52, and has consistently shown its effectiveness in the maritime surveillance role. During the Cold War, Bears making the long transit from Murmansk to Cuba nonstop and without refuelling were a frequent sight; few other aircraft could have matched that.

This Tupolev Tu-95MS-16 'Bear-H' is able to carry air-launched cruise missiles.

Myasishchev M-4 Bison

The production of the Soviet Union's first strategic jet bombers was entrusted to the Tupolev and Myasishchev design bureaux; the latter's efforts culminated in the four-engined Mya-4, given the NATO reporting name 'Bison'.

COUNTRY OF ORIGIN: USSR

TYPE: multi-role reconnaissance bomber

POWERPLANT: four 13,000kg (28,660lb) Soloviev D-15 turbojets

PERFORMANCE: maximum speed 900km/h (560mph); service ceiling 15,000m (49,200ft); range with 4,500kg (9920lb) of electronic gear or bombs 11,000km (6835 miles)

WEIGHTS: empty 80,000kg (176,400lb); maximum loaded 170,000kg (375,000lb)

DIMENSIONS: span 50.48m (165ft 7.5in); length 47.2m (154ft 10in); height 14.1m (46ft); wing area 309sq m (3,326.16sq ft)

ARMAMENT: six 23mm cannon in two forward turrets and tail turret; internal bay with provision over 4500kg (10,000lb) of stores

The M-4 Bison is seen here alongside another Myasishchev aircraft, the M-55, designed for high-altitude reconnaissance.

A single example of this large aircraft took part in the 1954 May Day parade over Moscow. It was expected to appear in large numbers in the inventories of the various Soviet air arms, but nothing was heard of it in the West for years. In fact the aircraft was produced in some numbers as the 'Bison-A' strategic bomber, and in 1959 a modified example set up new payload-to-height records. The Mya-4 bombers were subsequently adapted to the role of long-range strategic reconnaissance and ECM duties. In the 'Bison-C' sub-type a large search radar was fitted inside a lengthened and modified nose. The 'C' model was most frequently encountered on high- and low-level missions over the Arctic, and the Atlantic and Pacific oceans. Soviet bomber aircraft in operation during the 1960s wore a natural finish.

Operational four-engined jet bomber

Never a huge success in the long-range strategic bombing role for which it was intended, the Mya-4 was nevertheless the Soviet Union's first operational four-engined jet bomber, roughly comparable with early versions of the Boeing B-52. Its main role was maritime and electronic reconnaissance, with some used as flight refuelling tankers.

This illustration clearly shows the Bison's bogie-style undercarriage, with wingtip outriggers.

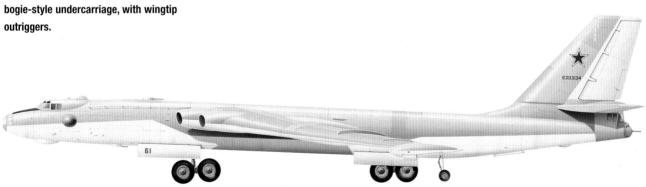

Douglas A-4 Skyhawk

In 1950, design studies began of a turbojet-powered shipboard attack aircraft capable of delivering nuclear weapons and performing a wide variety of conventional attack missions. The result was the XA4D-1 Skyhawk.

COUNTRY OF ORIGIN: USA

TYPE: jet fighter–bomber

POWERPLANT: one 3855kg (8500lb) thrust Pratt & Whitney J52-P-6 turbojet engine

PERFORMANCE: maximum speed 1102km/h (685mph); range 1480km (920 miles); service ceiling 14,935m (49,000ft)

DIMENSIONS: span 8.38m (27ft 6in); length 12.21m (40ft 1in); height 4.62m (15ft 2in)

WEIGHT: 11,113kg (24,500lb) loaded

ARMAMENT: two 20mm (0.79in) cannon; 3719kg (8200lb) of external ordnance

Few other jet aircraft have such an excellent combat record as the versatile A-4 Skyhawk.

The first of 165 A4D-1 Skyhawks were delivered to Attack Squadron VA-27 on 27 September 1956 and were replaced on the production line by the A4D-2, of which 542 were built. Plans had been made to re-engine the Skyhawk with the Pratt & Whitney J52-P-2 turbojet as the A4D-3, but this variant was cancelled and the next Skyhawk to appear was the A4D-2N, which had a lengthened nose to accommodate terrain clearance radar. The variant also featured a rocket-boosted low-level ejection seat. Deliveries to the USN began in 1959 and ended in 1962 after 638 aircraft had been built.

Variant attack bombers

The 1000th production Skyhawk was delivered in February 1961, and in July that year another variant, the A4D-5 (later redesignated A-4E) appeared (500 built), with an uprated engine, greater offensive load and a 27 per cent range increase. The next variant, the A-4F, was an attack bomber with a J52-P-8A turbojet, heavily armoured cockpit and updated avionics housed in a 'hump' aft of the cockpit. Production was completed in 1968 with 146 machines. The TA-4F was a tandem two-seat trainer, and the A-4G and TA-4G were similar aircraft supplied to the Royal Australian Navy. The A-4H was a variant supplied to Israel, the TA-4J was a simplified version of the TA-4F, the A-4K was a variant for the RNZAF, and the A-4M was developed for the USMC. During the 1960s the Skyhawk equipped some 40 USN and USMC squadrons, and saw extensive action in Vietnam. About 40 per cent of Israel's Skyhawks were lost during the Yom Kippur war of 1973, but this attrition was made good by the delivery of A-4N Skyhawk IIs, a light attack version. The A-4Y was an updated A-4M for the USMC. Skyhawks were supplied to Argentina, which used them during the Falklands War of 1982.

The Royal Australian Navy took delivery of 16 A-4E/F Skyhawks and four TA-4s, these being designated A-4G and TA-4G in Australian service.

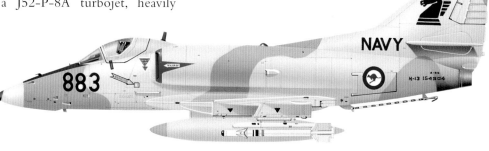

Republic F-105 Thunderchief

The F-105 was designed at a time when the USAF was giving top priority to building up its nuclear forces, and was intended from the outset to deliver tactical nuclear weapons.

Nicknamed the 'Thud', the F-105 Thunderchief suffered serious losses in Vietnam.

COUNTRY OF ORIGIN: USA

TYPE: (I-15ter) single-seat fighter and fighter-bomber

POWERPLANT: one 11,113kg (24,500lb) thrust Pratt & Whitney J75-19W turbojet engine

PERFORMANCE: maximum speed 2382km/h (1480mph); combat radius 370km (230 miles); service ceiling 15,850m (52,000ft)

WEIGHTS: 23,834kg (52,546lb) loaded

DIMENSIONS: span 10.65m (34ft 11in); length 19.58m (64ft 3in); height 5.99m (19ft 8in)

ARMAMENT: one 20mm (0.79in) M61 cannon; provision for up to 3629kg (8000lb) of bombs internally and 2722kg (6000lb) externally

Otherwise known as the I-15ter, the I-153 was first flown in 1938 as an attempt to modernize the I-15bis by reducing drag. In this capacity the two most important changes were a reversion to the type of gulled upper wing used on the I-15, and the introduction of manually operated retractable main landing-gear units. The type was built to the extent of 3437 aircraft and entered service in time for participation in the border incident with Japan in the summer of 1939. The type was also heavily involved in the Russo-Finnish 'Winter War' of 1939-40, and in the first part of the German invasion of the USSR from June 1941. The surviving I-153 aircraft were relegated to training service from the middle of 1943, although the Finns used captured aircraft as first-line fighters into 1944.

A challenge to fly

The aircraft was flown with some success by experienced pilots, but novice aviators found it a handful. This variant, which first flew on 9 June 1959 and entered service with Tactical Air Command the following year, embodied what was at the time the most advanced automatic navigation system in the world. For the largest and heaviest single-seat fighter-bomber in the world, the F-105 showed an astonishing ability to absorb battle damage and still get back to base. However, 397 F-105s were lost on operations in Vietnam, an attrition rate that earned the F-105 the nickname of 'Thud' (the noise of a crashing aircraft). A two-seat version, the F-105F, assumed the 'Wild Weasel' defence suppression role. F-105Fs fitted with improved defence suppression equipment were designated F-105G.

This is an F-105 Thunderchief of the 563rd 'Ace of Spades' Tactical Fighter Squadron, Tan Son Nhut AB, Thailand, 1965.

Convair B-58A Hustler

The Convair B-58 prototype flew on 11 November 1956. It was anticipated that the type would replace the B-47, but in the event only two Bomb Wings, the 43rd and 305th, were equipped with it.

COUNTRY OF ORIGIN: USA

TYPE: three-seat supersonic bomber

POWERPLANT: four 7076kg (15,600lb) General Electric J79-5B turbojets

PERFORMANCE: maximum speed 2125km/h (1385mph); service ceiling 19,500m (64,000ft); range on internal fuel 8248km (5125 miles)

WEIGHTS: empty 25,200kg (55,560lb); maximum take-off 73,930kg (163,000lb)

DIMENSIONS: span 17.31m (56ft 10in); length 29.5m (96ft 9in); height 9.6m (31ft 5in); wing area 145.32sq m (1542sq ft)

ARMAMENT: one 20mm T171 Vulcan rotary cannon in radar-aimed tail barbette, plus nuclear or conventional weapons in disposable underfuselage pod

A B-58 of the 43rd Bomber Wing thunders into the air while another taxies to the runway.

The B-58 was a historic aircraft on many counts. It was the first supersonic bomber and the first to reach Mach 2. It was the first aircraft constructed mainly from a stainless-steel honeycomb sandwich, the first to have a slim body and fat payload pod so that when the load was dropped, the aircraft became slimmer and lighter, the first to have stellar-inertial navigation, and the first weapon system to be procured as a single package from the prime contractor.

Overcoming technical problems

The technical problems in realizing the aircraft were daunting, yet the aircraft was developed with admirable speed and success. The first flight was made on November 11, 1956. The first production aircraft was delivered in September 1959, and the type entered service with the 43rd Bomber Wing of SAC in March 1960. However with increasing reliance on the ballistic missile submarine fleet for deterrence, the USAF retired the B-58 in 1970. The B-58 was a bold departure from conventional design. The three-man crew occupied tandem cockpits, and the B-58 was the first aircraft ever in which the crew had individual escape capsules for use at supersonic speeds. The only production version was the B-58A; 103 were built, eight converted to TB-58 trainers. During a career lasting ten years, from 1960–70, the B-58 established several records.

The B-58 was a radical aircraft, but it paid for its innovative design with a serious accident rate.

Blackburn (BAe) Buccaneer

This bomber was designed in 1954 to meet a Royal Navy requirement for a high-speed strike aircraft capable of operating from existing carriers and having sufficient firepower to destroy major Soviet surface units.

COUNTRY OF ORIGIN: United Kingdom

TYPE: two-seat attack aircraft

POWERPLANT: two 5105kg (11,255lb) Rolls-Royce RB.168 Spey Mk 101 turbofans

PERFORMANCE: maximum speed at 61m (200ft) 1040km/h (646mph); service ceiling over 12,190m (40,000ft); combat range with typical weapons load 3701km (2300 miles)

WEIGHTS: empty 13,608kg (30,000lb); maximum take-off 28,123kg (62,000lb)

DIMENSIONS: span 13.41 (44ft); length 19.33m (63ft 5in); height 4.97m (16ft 3in); wing area 47.82sq m (514.7sq ft)

ARMAMENT: four 454kg (1000lb) bombs, fuel tank, or reconnaissance pack on inside of rotary bomb door, four underwing pylons with provision for up to 5443kg (12,000lb) of bombs or missiles, including Harpoon and Sea Eagle anti-shipping missiles, and Martel anti-radar missiles

The Buccaneer could be difficult to handle at low speeds, but at high speed and low level it was superb.

After the Defence White Paper of April 1957, which proclaimed manned combat aircraft obsolete, the only British aircraft to avoid cancellation was the Blackburn B.103, the first to be designed specifically for carrier-borne strike operations at below radar level. The S.1 was marginal on power, but the greatly improved S.2 was a reliable and formidable aircraft. The first 84 were ordered by the Royal Navy.

Martel anti-radar missile carriers

A programme of substantial modification was carried out on the existing S.2 fleet, with a further 43 aircraft delivered from new. The primary difference with these aircraft, designated S.2B, was the provision to carry the Martel anti-radar missile. The Buccaneer replaced the English Electric Canberra in the low-level strike role, filling the gap created by the cancellation of the BAC TSR-2. The aircraft had an excellent low-level performance, being very gust-responsive. In the tactical nuclear role, it could carry the British 'Red Beard' nuclear weapon. Sixteen S.2s were also supplied to the South African Air Force, these being fitted with an auxiliary rocket motor to improve 'hot and high' take-off. Some were equipped with a TIALD (Thermal Imaging And Laser Designation Pod) and deployed to the Gulf, where they gave good service. The S.2 was retired in the mid-1990s.

This is a Buccaneer S.2B of No. 16 Squadron RAF, which operated the type from Laarbruch in Germany. Five RAF squadrons were armed with the Buccaneer.

Tupolev Tu-22 Blinder

The Tupolev Tu-22 Blinder, designed as a supersonic successor to the Badger, was first seen publicly at the Tushino air display in 1961. Its advanced design came as a shock to Western observers.

A Soviet Naval Air Arm Tu-22 about to touch down at an air base on the Murmansk peninsula.

COUNTRY OF ORIGIN: USSR

TYPE: medium bomber and missile-launch platform

POWERPLANT: two 16,000kg (35,273lb) Koliesov VD-7M turbojets

PERFORMANCE: maximum speed 1487km/h (924mph); service ceiling 18,300m (60,040ft); range with maximum fuel 3100km (1926 miles)

WEIGHTS: empty 40,000kg (88,185lb); maximum take-off 84,000lb (185,188lb)

DIMENSIONS: span 23.75m (77ft 11in); length 40.53m (132ft 11.75in); height 10.67m (35ft); wing area 162sq m (1,722.28sq ft)

ARMAMENT: one 23mm NR-23 cannon in tail turret; internal bomb bay with provision for up to 12,000kg (26,455lb) of conventional or nuclear bombs; or one AS-4 'Kitchen' air-to-surface missile semi-recessed under the fuselage

The 'Blinder-A' was built in response to the growing capability of Western manned interceptors and surface-to-air missile systems in the early 1950s. Soviet aviation planners were convinced the days of the Tupolev Tu-16 as a viable strategic bomber were numbered. The result was the Tu-22, the prototype of which is believed to have flown in 1959. Western analysts were completely unaware of this aircraft until 10 took part in the 1961 air display at Tushino in 1961. This ignorance is not really surprising, as at first glance the Tu-22 appears to be of similar basic configuration to the Tu-16 with a mid-set swept wing, all-swept tail surfaces and the main units of its tricycle landing gear retracting into wing pods. However, the wing differs considerably from that of the Tu-16 in having compound sweep on the leading edge and less anhedral.

First operational version

The Tu-22s seen at Tushino were pre-series trials aircraft, and first deliveries of the type to the Dalnaya Aviatsiya (Soviet Strategic Air Force) were not made until the following year. The first operational version, code-named Blinder-A, was produced in limited numbers only. The second variant, the Tu-22K Blinder-B, was equipped with a flight refuelling probe; 12 aircraft were supplied to Iraq and 24 to Libya. The Tu-22R Blinder-C was a dedicated maritime reconnaissance variant, about 60 of which were built, and the Tu-22P Blinder-E was an ECM aircraft.

Soviet Naval Air Arm Tu-22s were fitted with flight refuelling probes, seen here, to extend their radius of action.

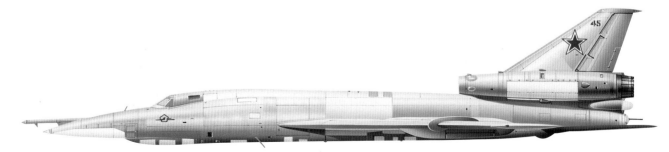

Grumman Intruder

Designed specifically as a carrier-based low-level attack bomber with the ability to deliver both nuclear and conventional warloads with pinpoint accuracy in all weathers.

COUNTRY OF ORIGIN: USA

TYPE: two-seat carrier-borne and landbased all-weather strike aircraft

POWERPLANT: two 4218kg (9300lb) Pratt & Whitney J52-P-8A turbojets

PERFORMANCE: maximum speed at sea level 1043km/h (648mph); service ceiling 14,480m (47,500ft); range with full weapon load 1627km (1011 miles)

WEIGHTS: empty 12,132kg (26,746lb); maximum take-off 26,581kg (58,600lb) for carrier launch or 27,397kg (60,400lb) for field take-off

DIMENSIONS: span 16.15m (53ft); length 16.69m (54ft 9in); height 4.93m (16ft 2in); wing area 49.13sq m (528.9sq ft)

ARMAMENT: five external hardpoints with provision for up to 8165kg (18,000lb) of stores, including nuclear weapons, guided and conventional bombs, air-to-surface missiles, and drop tanks

The Grumman A-6 Intruder brought a new dimension to the US Navy's ability to hit precision targets in all weather conditions.

The aircraft was designed to be subsonic and is powered by two straight turbojets. In the original design the efflux was routed through tilting jetpips to enhance STOL capabilities. Despite its considerable gross weight the Intruder has excellent slow-flying qualities with full span slats and flaps. The broad canopy gives the crew a good all-round view. The navigator controls one of the most sophisticated avionics suites on any current aircraft. The Intruder first came into service with the US Navy in February 1963; during the Vietnam War the A-6A was tasked with round-the-clock precision bombing missions that no other aircraft was capable of undertaking until the introduction of the F-111. The A-6A prototype flew on

19 April 1960 and the first operational aircraft entered service with Attack Squadron VA-42 on 1 February 1963.

Electronic warfare aircraft

The last delivery took place in December 1969, after 488 had been built. The A-6A saw extensive action over Vietnam, working round the clock and performing combat missions that were far beyond the capability of any other aircraft until the advent of the F-111, and also participated in the strike on Libya in April 1986. The next variant was the EA-6A, (27 produced for the US Marine Corps); this was followed by the EA-6B Prowler, with advanced avionics and a longer nose section to accommodate two extra ECM specialists.

The close of 1996 saw the end of the A-6's 31-year combat career with the US Navy, the type being deemed too expensive to operate in a service forced to cut back on its front-line types and one whose deep-strike mission had become less important in the post-Cold War world.

BAC TSR-2

Originally designed by English Electric to Operational Requirement 339, and developed jointly with Vickers-Armstrong, the TSR-2 was intended as a replacement for the English Electric Canberra.

COUNTRY OF ORIGIN: United Kingdom

TYPE: two-seat strike/reconnaissance aircraft

POWERPLANT: two 13,884kg (30,610lb) thrust Bristol Siddeley Olympus 320 turbojets

PERFORMANCE: maximum speed at altitude 2390km/h (1485mph); maximum speed 1345km/h (836mph) at 61m (200ft); operating ceiling 16,460m (54,000ft); range at low level 1287km (800 miles)

WEIGHTS: average mission take-off 36,287kg (80,000lb); maximum take-off 43,545kg (96,000lb)

DIMENSIONS: span 11.28m (37ft); length 27.13m (89ft); height 7.32m (24ft); wing area 65.03sq m (700sq ft)

ARMAMENT: (planned) up to 2722kg (6000lb) of conventional or nuclear weapons in an internal weapons bay; four underwing pylons for up to 1814kg (4000lb) of weapons

This image does not give an accurate impression of the TSR-2's size. It was a big aircraft, as large as the Canberra it was to have replaced.

At the time, the cancellation of the TSR.2 program was widely regarded within the aviation industry as the greatest disaster to befall the post-war British aviation industry. In retrospect it is clear that much of the pioneering research carried out by the project team was of great benefit during the development of Concorde.

Tactical strike and reconnaissance

The aircraft was designed by a combined English Electric and Vickers Armstrong to an RAF requirement issued in 1957 for a high-speed low-level tactical strike and reconnaissance aircraft. The aircraft that emerged represented a huge leap in airframe, avionics, engine, and equipment technology; XR219 first flew on 27 September 1964. Just four were built, although XR219 was the only example to fly. A remarkable aircraft, at the very cutting edge of aviation technology, TSR-2 had the most advanced nav/attack system in the world, and would have been able to deliver its weapons with pinpoint accuracy. A contract was placed for nine development TSR-2s in October 1960 and by the time the prototype made its first flight four more aircraft were in various stages of construction. On 6 April 1965, however, the whole programme was cancelled.

The TSR-2 was bedevilled by the fact that its development was controlled by a series of committees, which ruined the prospects of a very fine aircraft being created.

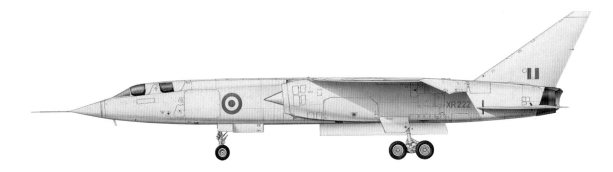

North American XB-70 Valkyrie

The North American XB-70A was originally planned as a long-range, high- and low-altitude supersonic bomber, but was relegated to a research role in 1961.

COUNTRY OF ORIGIN: USA

TYPE: long-range strategic bomber

POWERPLANT: six 14,074kg (31,000lb) General Electric YJ93-GE-3 turbojets

PERFORMANCE: maximum speed at 24,400m (80,000ft) 3185km/h (1,980mph); service ceiling 24,400m (80,000ft); range 12,067km (7500 miles)

WEIGHTS: maximum loaded 238,350kg (525,000lb)

DIMENSIONS: span 32.03m (105ft); length 57.64m (189ft); height 9.15m (30ft); wing area 585.62sq m (6,297sq ft)

The XB-70 approaching to land. The supersonic bomber was a complex and radical design.

One of the most impressive aircraft ever built, the XB-70 was a large delta-wing Mach 3 strategic bomber designed to replace Strategic Air Command B-52s in service in the mid-1960s. The initial US Air Force requirement was issued in 1954, and the North American design was selected for development in 1957. Budgetary cutbacks meant that by 1959 the programme had been reduced to a single prototype, but this was partially restored in 1960 with a further $265 million made available for development. In March 1961 President John F. Kennedy asked for a reduction in the XB-70 programme, citing several factors that included the high cost of developing the aircraft, its greater vulnerability compared with that of

The XB-70A exceeded Mach 3 for the first time in January 1966. Test flying continued until 4 February 1969, when the surviving XB-70A made its last flight.

strategic missiles, and its late projected in-service date, which now coincided with that of operational ICBMs. The B-70 strategic bomber project was subsequently discontinued, although two prototypes were built for research purposes.

Forward air control role

The first prototype flew in September 1964, with Mach 3 achieved just over 12 months later. Tragically, the second prototype was lost in a mid-air collision with an F-104 chase aircraft in June 1966. The surviving aircraft passed to NASA and the programme was terminated in 1969.

General Dynamics F-111

The F-111 was borne when the General Dynamics Corporation, in association with Grumman Aircraft, was selected to develop a variable-geometry tactical fighter to meet the requirements of the USAF's TFX programme.

COUNTRY OF ORIGIN: USA

TYPE: two-seat multi-purpose attack aircraft

POWERPLANT: two 11,385kg (25,100lb) Pratt & Whitney TF-30-P100 turbofans

PERFORMANCE: maximum speed at optimum altitude 2655km/h (1650mph); service ceiling above 17,985m (59,000ft); range with internal fuel 4707km (2925 miles)

WEIGHTS: empty 21,398kg (47,175lb); maximum take-off 45,359kg (100,000lb)

DIMENSIONS: span unswept 19.20m (63ft); swept 9.74m (32ft 11.5in); length 22.40m (73ft 6in); height 5.22m (17ft 1.5in); wing area 48.77sq m (525sq ft) unswept

ARMAMENT: one 20mm multi-barrelled M61A-1 cannon and one 340kg (750lb) B43 bomb, or two B43 bombs in internal bay, eight underwing hardpoints with provision for 14,290kg (31,000lb) of stores, inner four pivot to keep stores in alignment as wings sweep

An F-111 of the 48th TFW flares out for a landing at Lakenheath, Suffolk.

One hundred and sixty production F-111As were built, the first examples entering service with the 4480th Tactical Fighter Wing at Nellis AFB, Nevada, in October 1967. On 17 March 1968 six aircraft from this unit flew to Takhli AFB in Thailand for operational evaluation in Vietnam, making their first sorties on 25 March. The operation ended unhappily when three of the aircraft were lost as a result of metal fatigue in a control rod, but the problem was rectified and in September 1972 the F-111As of the 429th and 430th Tactical Fighter Squadrons deployed to Takhli and performed very effective service in the closing air offensive of the war (Linebacker II), attacking targets in the Hanoi area at night and in all weathers through the heaviest anti-aircraft concentrations

in the history of air warfare. The F-111E variant, which superseded the F-111A in service, featured modified air intakes to improve performance above 2.2M.

Working for NATO

Re-equipment of the 20th TFW at Upper Heyford in the UK was completed in the summer of 1971 and the unit was assigned the war role of interdicting targets deep inside hostile territory as part of NATO's 2nd Allied Tactical Air Force. The other UK-based F-111 TFW was the 48th; based at Lakenheath in Suffolk, yet it had the ability to interdict targets as far away as the Adriatic. The 48th TFW was armed with the F-111F, a fighter-bomber variant combining the best features of the F-111E and the FB-111A and fitted with the more powerful TF30-F-100 engines. The 48th TFW's aircraft were equipped to carry two B43 nuclear stores internally, as well as a variety of ordnance under six wing hardpoints, and formed the core of NATO's theatre nuclear strike force.

Its 'nose-to-the-ground' appearance earned the F-111 the nickname 'aardvark'.

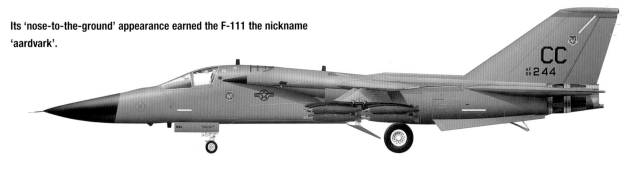

SEPECAT Jaguar

When Britain and France decided to contribute personnel and material to Operation Desert Storm in 1991, it was inevitable that the Jaguar should be included in the Coalition Forces' Order of Battle.

COUNTRY OF ORIGIN: France and United Kingdom

TYPE: single-seat tactical support and strike aircraft

POWERPLANT: two 3313kg (7305lb) Rolls-Royce/Turbomeca Adour Mk 102 turbofans

PERFORMANCE: maximum speed at 11,000m (36,090ft) 1593km/h (990mph); combat radius on lo-lo-lo mission with internal fuel 557km (357 miles)

WEIGHTS: empty 7000kg (15,432lb); maximum take-off 15,500kg (34,172lb)

DIMENSIONS: span 8.69m (28ft 6in); length 16.83m (55ft 2.5in); height 4.89m (16ft 0.5in); wing area 24sq m (258.34sq ft)

ARMAMENT: two 30mm DEFA cannon with 150 rpg; five external hardpoints with provision for 4536kg (10,000lb) of stores, including one AN-52 tactical nuclear weapon or conventional loads such as one AS.37 Martel anti-radar missile and two drop tanks, or eight 454kg (1000lb) bombs, or combinations of ASMs, drop tanks and rocket-launcher pods, and a reconnaissance pod

A SEPECAT Jaguar of the Indian Air Force cruising high above the clouds.

Developed jointly by the British Aircraft Corporation and Breguet (later Dassault-Breguet), the Jaguar emerged from protracted development as a much more powerful and effective aircraft than originally envisaged. The first French version to fly, in September 1968, was the two-seat E model, 40 being ordered by the French Air Force, followed in March 1969 by the single-seat Jaguar A tactical support aircraft. Service deliveries of the E began in May 1972, the first of 160 Jaguar As following in 1973. The British versions, known as the Jaguar S (strike) and Jaguar B (trainer), flew on October 12 1969 and 30 August 1971 respectively, being delivered to the RAF as the Jaguar GR.Mk.1(165 examples) and T.Mk.2 (38 examples).

The British Jaguars were fitted with two weapon guidance systems: a Laser Ranging and Marked Target Seeker (LRMTS) and a Navigation and Weapon Aiming Subsystem (NAVWASS), both developed by Ferranti.

Remarkable technology

At the time, the system, with its E3R inertial platform and MSC920M computer, seemed remarkable, giving a single-seat fighter pilot the best possible chance of making a first-pass attack without reference to tactical air navigation (TACAN) equipment or any other external aid. The Jaguar International, first flown in August 1976, was developed for the export market. It was purchased by Ecuador (12), Nigeria (18) and Oman (24) and was licence-built in India by HAL (98, including 40 delivered by B.Ae).

Seen here is a Royal Air Force Jaguar in desert camouflage and armed with Sidewinder AAMs.

Sukhoi Su-24 Fencer

The Su-24 Fencer, roughly the equivalent of America's F-111, would have caused serious problems for NATO's air defences in the event of a war.

In 1965, the Soviet government prompted Sukhoi to design a new Soviet variable geometry attack aircraft comparable in performance to the F-111. One of the primary requirements for the new aircraft was the ability to penetrate increasingly efficient radar defences by flying at very low level and at supersonic speeds. It was also specified that the aircraft should be able to operate from short, unpaved airstrips. Initial development of a VTOL aircraft to meet these criteria was halted, and work began to develop the swing-wing aircraft, designated Su-24, which emerged to make its first flight in 1970. Service deliveries of the 'Fencer A' began in 1974.

COUNTRY OF ORIGIN: USSR

TYPE: two-seat strike and attack aircraft

POWERPLANT: two 11,250kg (24,802lb) Lyul'ka AL-21F-3A turbojets

PERFORMANCE: maximum speed above 11,000m (36,090ft) approximately 2316km/h (1,439mph); service ceiling 17,500m (57,415ft); combat radius on hi-lo-hi mission with 3000kg (6614lb) load 1050km (650 miles)

WEIGHTS: empty 19,000kg (41,888lb); maximum take-off 39,700kg (87,520lb)

DIMENSIONS: span 17.63m (57ft 10in) spread and 10.36m (34ft) swept; length 24.53m (80ft 5in); height 4.97m (16ft 0.75in); wing area 42sq m (452.1sq ft)

ARMAMENT: one 23mm GSh-23-6 six-barrelled cannon; nine external pylons with provision for up to 8000kg (17,635lb) of stores, including nuclear weapons, air-to-air missiles, air-to-surface missiles such as the AS-14 'Kedge', guided bombs, cluster bombs, dispenser weapons, large-calibre rockets, rocket-launcher pods, drop tanks and ECM pods

The Su-24 Fencer is a very capable aircraft and has sufficient range to strike at targets well outside Russian territory.

This image of a Fencer approaching to land shows the aircraft's extensive flap area.

The 'Fencer D' (Su-24M), which entered service in 1986, is an improved version with inflight refuelling equipment, upgraded nav/attack systems, Kaira laser and TV designator and improved defensive aids.

Saturation attacks

On exercises, the Su-24s operate in cells of four aircraft, making saturation attacks on targets rather than attacking individually. The usual mix of aircraft on a deployment exercise might include six Tupolev Tu-95 bombers, ten Su-24 attack aircraft and four Sukhoi Su-27 escort fighters, these being supported by twelve Il-78 flight refuelling tankers, one A-50 AWACS and two airborne command posts. On one exercise, Voskhod-93, which began on 18 May 1993, a mix of aircraft described above departed from three airfields in western Russia at 01.00 hours local time, heading for the Amur training area in the far to the east. The ten Su-24s refuelled twice during the 5000-mile flight, which was accomplished in twelve and a half hours, while the Su-27s refuelled at airfields en route.

Tupolev Tu-22M Backfire

The mission of the Tu-22M Backfire, peripheral attack or intercontinental attack, became one of the most fiercely contested intelligence debates of the Cold War.

COUNTRY OF ORIGIN: USSR

TYPE: medium strategic bomber and maritime reconnaissance/patrol aircraft

POWERPLANT: two (estimated) 20,000kg (44,092lb) Kuznetsov NK-144 turbofans

PERFORMANCE: maximum speed 2125km/h (1321mph); service ceiling 18,000m (59,055ft); combat radius with internal fuel 4000km (2485 miles)

WEIGHTS: maximum take-off 130,000kg (286,596lb)

DIMENSIONS: span 34.3m (112ft 6.5in) spread and 23.4m (76ft 9.25in) swept; length 36.9m (129ft 11in); height 10.8m (35ft 5.25in); unswept wing area 183.58sq m (1892 q ft)

ARMAMENT: two 23mm GSh-23 two-barrel cannon in radar-controlled tail barbette; internal weapons bay with provision for 12,000kg (26,455lb) of stores, including nuclear weapons and free-fall bombs, or two AS-4 'Kitchen' missiles carried under the wings, or one AS-4 carried semi-recessed under the fuselage, or up to three AS-16 missiles

A Tu-22M flying at low speed with its variable-geometry wings fully extended.

The Tu-22M 'Backfire' began life as a swing-wing derivative of the Tu-22 'Blinder' supersonic bomber and maritime patrol aircraft. The inability of this aircraft to fly strategic missions to the US (because of short range) led the Tupolev bureau to produce the 'Backfire-A' prototype (designated Tu-22M).

Speed and range shortcomings
The aircraft fell far short of expectations, both in terms of speed and range, leading to the major design revisions incorporated on the Tu-22M-2. This aircraft entered service in 1975 and has the NATO reporting name 'Backfire-B'. Some 360 were manufactured in M-2 and M-3 configuration for Long Range Aviation and Naval Aviation units and were expected to remain in service, but it would appear that the M-2 aircraft have all been retired or placed into storage. The M3 (Backfire-C) variant had reduced defensive armament and the flight refuelling probe was deleted; a reconnaissance version, the Tu-22MR, entered service in 1985, and the Tu-22ME is the latest of the attack variants. In the Cold War, saturation tactics by missile-armed Backfires posed a real and potentially devastating threat to NATO's surface task grfoups. Although the Cold War era is at an end, the Backfire still provides Russia with a credible anti-shipping strike force.

With flight refuelling, the Backfire gave the former USSR a formidable strike capability far out into the Atlantic and Pacific Oceans. The light blue, two-tone colour scheme was retained after the disbandment of the Soviet Union.

Fairchild Republic A-10A Thunderbolt II

In general, operations by the A-10s envisaged cooperation with US Army helicopters who would leave the enemy's defences stunned or degraded, so the A-10s would be free to concentrate their fire on the tanks.

COUNTRY OF ORIGIN: USA

TYPE: single-seat close support aircraft

POWERPLANT: two 4112kg (9065lb) General Electric TF34-GE-100 turbofans

PERFORMANCE: maximum speed at sea level 706km/h (439mph); combat radius 402km (250 miles) for a 2-hour loiter with 18 Mk82 bombs plus 750 rounds cannon ammunition

WEIGHTS: empty 11,321kg (24,959lb); maximum take-off 22,680kg (50,000lb)

DIMENSIONS: span 17.53m (57ft 6in); length 16.26m (53ft 4in); height 4.47m (14ft 8in); wing area 47.01sq m (506sq ft)

ARMAMENT: one 30mm GAU-8/A rotary cannon with capacity for 1350 rounds of ammunition, eleven hardpoints with provision for up to 7528kg (16,000lb) of disposable stores; weapons include conventional bombs, incendiary bombs, Rockeye cluster bombs, AGM-65 Maverick air-to-surface missiles, laser and optronically guided bombs and SUU-23 20mm cannon pods

Nicknamed the 'Warthog', the A-10A Thunderbolt II was designed to survive in a hostile battlefield environment.

The Fairchild Republic A-10A grew out of the USAF's A-X programme of 1967, to produce a highly battleproof, heavily armed close air support aircraft to replace the A-1 Skyraider. In December 1970 three companies were chosen to build prototypes for evaluation and Fairchild's YA-10A emerged as the winner in January 1973.

A devastating bomber

Six pre-production aircraft were submitted for evaluation, resulting in a production contract for 52A-10As in December 1974. Some 727 were procured by the USAF. The A-10 was designed to operate from short, unprepared strips less than 457m (1500ft) long. Deliveries began in March 1977 to the 354th Tactical Fighter Wing at Myrtle Beach, South Carolina; in all, the USAF took delivery of 727 aircraft for service with its tactical fighter wings. The A-10 had a combat radius of 463km (250 miles), enough to reach a target area on the East German border from a Forward Operating Location in central Germany and then move on to another target area in northern Germany. The aircraft had a three and a half hour loiter endurance, although operational war sorties in Europe would probably have lasted between one and two hours. The A-10A has a huge GAU-8/A cannon, but the range of weaponry it can carry is devastating, as was proved during actions against Iraqi armour in the 1991 Gulf War. Since then the aircraft have been redesignated OA-10A to mark their forward air control role. Although the USAF wants to retire the aircraft, the OA-10A keeps proving its worth as a battlefield support tool, latterly in the 2003 war in Iraq.

Seen here is an A-10A of the 926th Fighter Squadron, New Orleans Air National Guard.

Panavia Tornado

The Tornado was the result of a 1960s requirement for a strike and reconnaissance aircraft capable of carrying a heavy and varied weapons load and of penetrating foreseeable Warsaw Pact defensive systems by day and night.

The Tornado eventually went a long way towards filling the gap left by the cancellation of TSR-2.

COUNTRY OF ORIGIN: Germany, Italy and UK

TYPE: multi-role combat aircraft

POWERPLANT: two 7292kg (16,075lb) Turbo-Union RB.199-34R Mk 103 turbofans

PERFORMANCE: maximum speed above 11,000m (36,090ft) 2337km/h (1,452mph); service ceiling 15,240m (50,000ft); combat radius with weapon load on hi-lo-hi mission 1390km (864 miles)

WEIGHTS: empty 14,091kg (31,065lb); maximum take-off 27,216kg (60,000lb)

DIMENSIONS: span 13.91m (45ft 7in) spread and 8.6m (28ft 2.5in) swept; length 16.72m (54ft 10in); height 5.95m (19ft 6.25in); wing area 26.60sq m (286.3sq ft)

ARMAMENT: two 27mm IWKA-Mauser cannon with 180 rpg, seven external hardpoints with provision for up to 9000kg (19,840lb) of stores, including nuclear and JP233 runway denial weapon, ALARM anti-radiation missiles, air-to-air, air-to-surface and anti-ship missiles, conventional and guided bombs, cluster bombs, ECM pods and drop tanks

A triumph of collaboration, the first of nine Tornado IDS (Interdictor/Strike) prototypes flew in Germany on 14 August 1974. Aircrews of the participating nations been trained at RAF Cottesmore in the UK, which received the first Tornado GR.1s in July 1980. The RAF took delivery of 229 GR.1 strike aircraft, the Luftwaffe 212, the German Naval Air Arm 112, and the Italian Air Force 100.

A wide range of roles

RAF and Italian Tornados saw action in the 1991 Gulf War. The Tornado GR.1A is a variant with a centreline reconnaissance pod, while the GR.4, armed with Sea eagle anti-shipping missiles, is an anti-shipping version, the GR.4A being the tactical reconnaissance equivalent. Forty-eight Tornado IDS were delivered to Saudi Arabia. In 1971, the UK Ministry of Defence issued Air Staff

Target 395, which called for a minimum-change, minimum-cost but effective interceptor to replace the British Aerospace Lightning and the F.4 Phantom in the air defence of the United Kingdom. Primary armament was to be the British Aerospace Dynamics XJ521 Sky Flash medium-range air-to-air missile, and the primary sensor was to be a Marconi Avionics pulse-Doppler radar. The result was the Air Defence Variant (ADV) of the Panavia Tornado interdictor/strike (IDS) aircraft. This variant served only with the RAF and the Italian Air Force.

The Tornado IDS appeared as the GR.1 in its RAF interdictor/strike role.

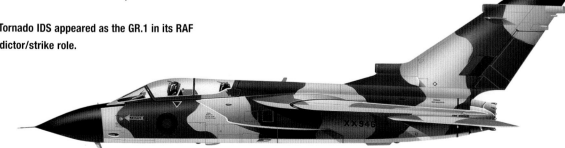

Rockwell B-1B Lancer

Designed to replace the B-52 and FB-111 in the low-level penetration role, the B-1 prototype flew on 23 December 1974, and subsequent flight trials and evaluation progressed rapidly.

COUNTRY OF ORIGIN: USA

TYPE: long-range multi-role strategic bomber

POWERPLANT: four 13,962kg (30,780lb) General Electric F101-GE-102 turbofans

PERFORMANCE: maximum speed at high altitude 1328km/h (825mph); service ceiling 15,240m (50,000ft); range on internal fuel 12,000km (7,455 miles)

WEIGHTS: empty 87,090kg (192,000lb); maximum take-off 216,634kg (477,000lb)

DIMENSIONS: span 41.67m (136ft 8.5in) unswept and 23.84m (78ft 2.5in) swept; length 44.81m (147ft); height 10.36m (34ft); wing area 181.16sq m (1,950sq ft)

ARMAMENT: three internal bays with provision for up to 34,019kg (75,000lb) of weapons, plus eight underfuselage stations with a capacity of 26,762kg (59,000lb); weapons can include AGM-69 SRAMs, AGM-86B ALCMs, B-28, B-43, B-61 or B-83 nuclear bombs, and Mk 82 or Mk 84 conventional bombs

Escalating costs almost defeated the Rockwell B-1 programme, but the aircraft survived.

The B-1B long-range penetration bomber was originally conceived in the 1965 USAF Advanced Manned Strategic Aircraft requirement. North American Rockwell were selected as the prime contractor for the new bomber, designated B-1. General Electric were selected to build the F101 engines to power it. Prototype contracts were awarded in June 1970, with planned service delivery of all 244 aircraft scheduled before 1981. The first prototype made its maiden flight on December 23, 1974, but the programme was cancelled in 1977 because of costs. A contract for 100 aircraft derived from the B-1, with a role as a cruise missile carrier, was awarded in 1982.

Forward air control role

Despite a series of problems with avionics and systems, B-1B deliveries to SAC reached a tempo of four per month in 1986. In January 1987 the trials aircraft successfully launched a SRAM, and in April an aircraft from the 96th BW completed a 21-hour 40-minute mission that involved five inflight refuellings, the aircraft flying at about 741km/h (460mph) and covering 15,148km (9407 miles). This operation was in connection with the development of operational techniques involving the carriage of very heavy loads over long distances. The aircraft incorporated a variable-geometry configuration with stealth technology and advanced avionics. All aircraft now wear a dark low-visibility camouflage scheme.

Seen here is a B-1B of the 28th Bomb Wing, Ellsworth AFB, South Dakota.

Sukhoi Su-25 Frogfoot-A

A Russian requirement for an attack aircraft in the A-10 Thunderbolt II class materialized in the Sukhoi Su-25 Frogfoot, which was selected in preference to a rival design, the Ilyushin Il-102.

COUNTRY OF ORIGIN: USSR

TYPE: single-seat close-support aircraft

POWERPLANT: two 4500kg (9921lb) Tumanskii R-195 turbojets

PERFORMANCE: maximum speed at sea level 975km/h (606mph); service ceiling 7,000m (22,965ft); combat radius on lo-lo-lo mission with 4400kg (9700lb) load 750km (466 miles)

WEIGHTS: empty 9,500kg (20,950lb); maximum take-off 17,600kg (38,800lb)

DIMENSIONS: span 14.36m (47ft 1.5in); length 15.53m (50ft 11.5in); height 4.8m (15ft 9in); wing area 33.7sq m (362.75sq ft)

ARMAMENT: one 30mm GSh-30-2 cannon with 250 rds; eight external pylons with provision for up to 4400kg (9700lb) of stores, including AAMs, ASMs, ARMs, anti-tank missiles, guided bombs, cluster bombs, dispenser weapons, large-calibre rockets, rocket-launcher pods, drop tanks and ECM pods

The Su-25 was designed to carry out a similar mission to the USAF's A-10, with high battlefield survivability.

Western intelligence sources first identified the Frogfoot at Ramenskoye test centre in 1977 and gave it the provisional US designation 'Ram-J'. The prototype first flew in 1975, and production of the single-seat close-support Su-25K began in 1978. The pilot sits in an armoured cockpit, and on the Su-25K had a Sirena-3 radar-warning system and tailcone mounted chaff/decoy flare dispenser to protect his aircraft. A nose-mounted laser range finder and marked target seeker reportedly allows bombing accuracy to within 5m (16ft) over a stand-off range of 20km (12.5 miles). A trial unit was deployed to Afghanistan as early as 1980, followed by a full squadron,

In service with the Soviet Air Force, the Su-25 was nicknamed Grach (Rook), and most aircraft deployed to Afghanistan featured a cartoon rook design. Russian infantrymen called the aircraft Rascheska (The Comb) because of its ten weapon pylons, which gave it a comb-like appearance when seen from below.

to support Soviet troops fighting in the mountainous country. The squadron worked closely with Mi-24 'Hind' gunships and the aircraft became fully operational in 1984.

Losses and lessons

An upgraded version known as the Su-25T was produced with improved defensive systems to counter weapons like the Stinger. The improvements included the insertion of steel plates, several millimetres thick, between the engine bays and below the fuel cell. After this modification no further Su-25s were lost to shoulder-launched missiles. In total, 22 Su-25s were lost in the nine years of the Afghan conflict. The Su-25UBK is a two-seat export variant, while the Su-25UBT is a navalized version with a strengthened undercarriage and arrester gear. The Su-25UT (Su-28) was a trainer version.

Lockheed F-117 Night Hawk

The amazing F-117A 'Stealth' aircraft began life in 1973 as a project called 'Have Blue', launched to study the feasibility of producing a combat aircraft with little or no radar and infrared signature.

COUNTRY OF ORIGIN: USA

TYPE: single-seat stealth-attack aircraft

POWERPLANT: two 4899kg (10,800lb) General Electric F404-GE-F1D2 turbofans

PERFORMANCE: maximum speed about Mach 1 at high altitude: combat radius about 1112km (691 miles) with maximum payload

WEIGHTS: empty about 13,608kg (30,000lb); maximum take-off 23,814kg (52,500lb)

DIMENSIONS: span 13.20m (43ft 4in); length 20.08m (65ft 11in); height 3.78m (12ft 5in); wing area about 105.9sq m (1,140sq ft)

ARMAMENT: provision for 2268kg (5000lb) of stores on rotary dispenser in weapon bay; including the AGM-88 HARM anti-radiation missile; AGM-65 Maverick ASM, GBU-19 and GBU-27 optronically guided bombs, BLU-109 laser-guided bomb, and B61 free-fall nuclear bomb

The Lockheed F-117A was the product of many years of experimentation, conducted in extreme secrecy.

The F-117 is probably the most important aircraft to enter service in the past two decades, and has redefined our concept of what the flying machine of the twenty-first century will look like. The development programme is shrouded in secrecy, but it is likely that research into stealth technology began in earnest in the wake of a number of successful radar guided missile attacks on US-built F-4s during the 1973 Yom Kippur war. Both Lockheed and Northrop submitted proposals for the Experimental Stealth Technology requirement issued by the DOD; Lockheed's proposal was subsequently selected in 1977.

This is an F-117A of the 37th Tactical Fighter Wing, which forms part of the USAF's rapid reaction force.

Primary attack weapon

The aircraft was delivered five years later. F-117As of the 37th Tactical Fighter Wing played a prominent part in the 1991 Gulf War, making first strikes on high priority targets; since then they have been used in the Balkans, Afghanistan and again in Iraq. The last of 59 F-117As was delivered in July 1990. Along with the Northrop Grumman B-2 Spirit 'stealth bomber', the Night Hawk is the USAF's primary attack weapon, the F-117 force being able to exert an influence on an air campaign that far outweighs its meagre size. As was seen during Desert Storm, the F-117's primary role is to attack high-value command, control and communications targets to, in effect, 'decapitate' the enemy's ability to control his forces Such targets include leadership bunkers, command posts and air defence and communications centres.

Tupolev Tu-160 Blackjack-A

The Tu-160 supersonic bomber first flew on 19 December 1981, but one of the two prototypes was lost in an accident. After the end of the Cold War it became an expensive 'white elephant'.

COUNTRY OF ORIGIN: USSR

TYPE: long-range stategic penetration bomber and missile platform

POWERPLANT: four 25,000kg (55,115lb) Kuznetsov NK-321 turbofans

PERFORMANCE: maximum speed at 11,000m (36,090ft) 2000km/h (1243mph); service ceiling 18,300m (60,040ft); combat range with internal fuel 14,000km (8699 miles)

WEIGHTS: empty 118,000kg (260,140lb); maximum take-off 275,000kg (606,261lb)

DIMENSIONS: span 55.70m (182ft 9in) spread and 35.60m (116ft 9.75in) swept; length 54.10m (177ft 6in); height 13.10m (43ft); wing area 360sq m (3875sq ft)

ARMAMENT: provision for up to 16,500kg (36,376lb) of stores in two internal weapons bays and on hardpoints under wings; including nuclear and/or free-fall bombs, and/or missiles including up to 12 RK-55 (AS-15 'Kent') cruise missiles or 24 RKV-500B (AS-16 'Kickback') short-range attack missiles

Like many aircraft projects in the former USSR, the Tu-160's development was conducted with undue haste.

The most recent and undoubtedly formidable aircraft to have emerged from the Tupolev Design Bureau is the Tu-160 long-range strategic bomber. Comparable to, although much larger than the Rockwell B1-B Lancer, the aircraft has variable-geometry outer wings and two pairs of afterburning turbofans in underwing nacelles. It is optimized for high-level penetration but also has a low-level terrain-following capability, and has a higher maximum speed and greater unrefuelled range than the B-1.

Arms limitation

Production of the aircraft, which entered service in 1988, has been curtailed by arms limitation agreements.

Those in service have suffered from serviceability problems and flight control system difficulties. Thirty-six aircraft (out of a planned total of 100, reduced after the collapse of the Soviet Union) were in service with the Soviet Air Force, these being divided between the 184th Air Regiment in the Ukraine and the 121st Air Regiment at Engels Air Base. The Ukraine-based aircraft were eventually returned to Russia, along with 600 air-launched missiles, as part of a deal which involved paying off a commercial debt.

The Tu-160 had a protracted development, with many pitfalls on the way, and it became superfluous after the collapse of the Soviet Union.

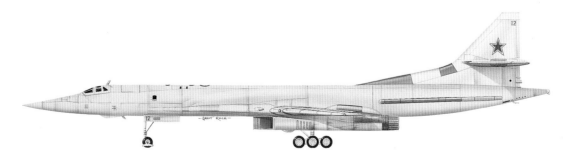

Northrop Grumman B-2 Spirit

In designing the B-2, the Northrop Company decided on an all-wing configuration from the outset. Flying-wing devotees such as Hugo Junkers and Jack Northrop have existed as long as aviation itself.

COUNTRY OF ORIGIN: USA

TYPE: strategic bomber and missile-launch platform

POWERPLANT: four 8618kg (19,000lb) General Electric F118-GE-110 turbofans

PERFORMANCE: maximum speed at high altitude 764km/h (475mph); service ceiling 15,240m (50,000ft); range on high level mission with standard fuel and 16,919kg (37,300lb) warload 11,675km (7255 miles)

WEIGHTS: empty 45,360kg (100,000lb); maximum take-off 181,437kg (400,000lb)

DIMENSIONS: span 52.43m (172ft); length 21.03m (69ft); height 5.18m (17ft); wing area more than 464.5sq m (5,000sq ft)

ARMAMENT: two internal bomb bays with provision for up to 22,680kg (50,000lb) of stores; each bay can carry one eight-round Boeing Rotary launcher for a total of 16 x 1.1 megaton B83 thermonuclear free-fall bombs, 22 x 680kg (1500lb) bombs, or 80 x 227kg (500lb) free-fall bombs

Northrop's flying wing designs of the late 1940s met with no success, but the concept was successfully resurrected in the amazing B-2.

The B-2 has been developed from 1978 to a US Air Force requirement for a strategic penetration bomber to complement and replace the Rockwell B-1 Lancer and the Boeing B-52 Stratofortress. It was built to incorporate low-observables (stealth technology), with Northrop as the prime contractor. The characteristic flying-wing stems from the extensive research carried out by the company in the 1940s. Northrop's experimental piston-engined flying wing bomber of the 1940s was designed to equal the range

and carry the same warload as the Convair B-36, but at two-thirds the gross weight and two-thirds the power.

An all-wing solution

In 1947 the company also built a prototype flying-wing jet bomber, the YB-49, but this had little influence on the decision to pursue an all-wing solution for the B-2; the all-wing approach was selected because it promised to result in a clean configuration for minimizing radar cross-section, including the elimination of vertical tail surfaces, with added benefits such as span-loading structural efficiency and high lift/drag ratio for efficient cruise.

The B-2, shown here, lifts off at 140kt (260km/h), the speed independent of take-off weight. Normal operating speed is in the high subsonic range and maxium altitude around 15,240m (50,000ft). It is highly manoeuvrable, with fighter-like handling characteristics.

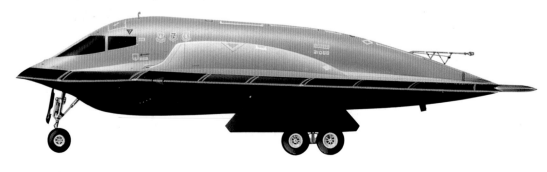

Glossary

AEW: Airborne Early Warning.

Afterburning (reheat): method of increasing the thrust of a gas turbine aircraft engine by injecting additional fuel into the hot exhaust duct between the engine and the tailpipe, where it ignites to provide a short-term increase of power.

All-Up Weight: the total weight of an aircraft in operating condition. Normal maximum AUW is the maximum at which an aircraft is permitted to fly within normal design restrictions, while overload weight is the maximum AUW at which an aircraft is permitted to fly subject to ultimate flying restrictions.

AMRAAM: Advanced Medium-Range Air-to-Air Missile.

Angle of Attack: the angle between the wing (airfoil) and the airflow relative to it.

Aspect Ratio: the ratio of wing span to chord

ASV: Air to Surface Vessel – airborne detection radar for locating ships and submarines.

Automatic Pilot (Autopilot): automatic device that keeps an aircraft flying on a set course at a set speed and altitude.

AWACS: Airborne Warning and Control System.

Basic Weight: the tare weight of an aircraft plus the specified operational load.

Centre of Gravity: point in a body through which the sum of the weights of all its parts passes. A body suspended from this point is said to be in a state of equilibrium.

Centre of Pressure: point through which the lifting force of a wing acts.

Chord: cross-section of a wing from leading edge to trailing edge.

Delta Wing: aircraft shaped like the Greek letter delta.

Disposable Load: the weight of crew and consumable load (fuel, missiles etc.).

Elevator: a horizontal control surface used to control the upward or downward inclination of an aircraft in flight. Elevators are usually hinged to the trailing edge of the tailplane.

ELF: Extremely Low Frequency. A radio frequency used for communication with submarines.

Empty Equipped (also known as Tare Weight): the weight of an aircraft equipped to a minimum scale, i.e. with all equipment plus the weight of coolant in the engines, radiators and associated systems, and residual fuel in tanks, engines and associated systems.

Gas turbine: engine in which burning fuel supplies hot gas to spin a turbine.

GPS: Global Positioning System. A system of navigational satellites.

GR: General Reconnaissance.

Laminar Flow: airflow passes over an aircraft's wing in layers, the first of which, the boundary layer, remains stationary while successive layers progressively accelerate; this is known as laminar flow. The smoother the wing surface, and the more efficient its design, the smoother the airflow.

Landing Weight: the AUW of an aircraft at the moment of landing.

Mach: named after the Austrian Professor Ernst Mach, a Mach number is the ratio of the speed of an aircraft or missile to the local speed of sound. At sea level, Mach One (1.0M) is approximately 1226 km/h (762mph), decreasing to about 1062 km/h (660mph) at 30,000 feet. An aircraft or missile travelling faster than Mach One is said to be supersonic.

Maximum Landing Weight: the maximum AUW, due to design or operational limitations, at which an aircraft is permitted to land.

Maximum Take-Off Weight: the maximum AUW, due to design or operational limitations, at which an aircraft is permitted to take off.

Megaton: Thermonuclear weapon yield, one megaton (mT) being roughly equal to 1,000,000 tons of TNT.

Muzzle Velocity: the speed at which a bullet or shell leaves a gun barrel.

NVG: Night Vision Goggles. Specially designed goggles that enhance a pilot's ability to see at night.

Operational Load: The weight of equipment necessarily carried by an aircraft for a particular role.

Payload: the weight of passengers and/or cargo

Ramjet: simple form of jet engine which is accelerated to high speed causing air to be forced into the combustion chamber, into which fuel is sprayed and then ignited.

Rudder: movable vertical surface or surfaces forming part of the tail unit, by which the yawing of an aircraft is controlled.

RWR: Radar Warning Receiver. A device mounted on an aircraft that warns the pilot if he is being tracked by an enemy missile guidance or intercept radar.

SAM: Surface-to-Air Missile.

Stall: condition that occurs when the smooth flow of the air over an aircraft's wing changes to a turbulent flow and the lift decreases to the point where control is lost.

Stealth Technology: technology applied to aircraft or fighting vehicles to reduce their radar signatures.

STOVL: Short Take-off, Vertical Landing.

Take-Off Weight: the AUW of an aircraft at the moment of take-off.

Thermal Imager: Equipment fitted to an aircraft or fighting vehicle which typically comprises a telescope to collect and focus infra-red energy emitted by objects on a battlefield, a mechanism to scan the scene across an array of heat-sensitive detectors, and a processor to turn the signals from these detectors into a 'thermal image' displayed on a TV screen.

Variable-Geometry Wing: a type of wing whose angle of sweep can be altered to suit a particular flight profile. Popularly called a Swing Wing.

VHF: Very High Frequency.

VLF: Very Low Frequency.

V/STOL: Vertical/Short Take-off and Landing.

Yaw: the action of turning an aircraft in the air around its normal (vertical) axis using the rudder.

Index